MORE
FUN
WITH
fIGURES

by
J. A. H. HUNTER

DOVER PUBLICATIONS, INC.
NEW YORK

Published in Canada by General Publishing Company, Ltd., 30 Lesmill Road, Don Mills, Toronto, Ontario.

Published in the United Kingdom by Constable and Company, Ltd., 10 Orange Street, London W. C. 2.

Library of Congress Catalog Card Number: 66-24127

Manufactured in the United States of America
Dover Publications, Inc.
180 Varick Street
New York, N. Y. 10014

CONTENTS

PREFACE

The immediate, and to me surprising, success of my previous book *Fun with Figures* is the excuse for producing this further selection of teasers. Again they are meant for people like myself who enjoy figures without being too serious about them.

Ideas from many kind readers have provided the basis for some. To those good friends and to the many thousands of others, known and unknown, whose interest and loyal support have made this book possible, I should like to say: 'Thank you!'

J. A. H. HUNTER

Toronto
1958

1. Walt's Waxworks

'Waxworks are a cinch!' said Walt after only two days in the business. He had started small, of course—just a one-room shop on a busy street in a drab district. But a flashy sign, lush and sexy and far removed from anything to be seen inside, brought in the people.

He was charging three rates, he said: top price for men, rather lower for women, and a nominal fee for a child. 'The first day was fine,' he told Jim, 'and I took in $20.10.' Fixing Lady Godiva's tresses, he went on: 'Yesterday, my second day, the same number of people came in but I took a dollar twenty less.'

'How come?' asked Jim, somewhat confused by what he saw.

'Same number of children as there'd been men the first day,' replied Walt, 'and of women as there'd been kids and of men as there'd been women.' He chuckled happily. 'It's the men I want, and if they'd all been men I'd have taken in thirty dollars yesterday.'

There's a streak of caution in Jim. 'What if they don't come?' he suggested.

Walt laughed. 'It wouldn't break me,' he boasted. 'If they'd all been women I'd have taken fifteen bucks each day, or six bucks even if they'd all been kids.'

Jim could hardly envisage the show as family entertainment, but he asked if there were any reduction in such cases. 'Not a cent,' declared Walt. 'Just regular rates: eighty-five cents for two parents with a child.'

At that moment a bunch of teenagers entered the place, so Jim went out. But he really would like to know how many men had gone there the first day. Maybe you know?

1

2. Two Friends on the Road

Bill drove to Exville last week from his home in Wyeville. His friend John, who lives in Exville, chose the same day to drive over to Wyeville and started from home fifty minutes after Bill had left his Wyeville home.

The new highway between the two villages is now open. They say too much has gone into the pockets of too many on its construction, but it's a fine road and fast, with a clear run all the way.

Just thirty-six miles short of Exville the two friends passed each other. Bill had been driving for ninety minutes. By a strange coincidence they reached their respective destinations at exactly the same time. Road maps aren't always reliable, but maybe you can figure out the distance between the two villages on the assumption that both drivers maintained steady speeds on the road that day.

3. Easy? Well, Maybe

This isn't really difficult, though it will require some very straight thinking. Each letter stands for a different figure, of course, and you have to find the meaning of AN EEL.

```
A N ) E E L ( O H
      L A
      M H L
      M N N
        A O
```

2

4. *Whose Glass Is It?*

'I'm mad at myself!' exclaimed Mary coming into the room with a large paper bag. 'There were some nice glasses at the store, and I picked some tumblers at nineteen cents and sherry glasses at twenty-nine.'

'Sounds reasonable,' remarked Doug. 'We certainly need more tumblers.'

'Yes, I know,' his wife sighed. 'But Susan came up and had to interfere—you know how she is. She persuaded me to get three more of the sherry glasses than I had intended, but no tumblers. And she also made me buy six of these silly markers.' Mary had been unpacking the bag as she spoke, and she now held up an attractive little clip in the shape of a heart. 'And I fell for her idea, as the whole lot came to one cent less than what I'd planned to buy.'

'But that's dandy,' laughed Doug, clipping the marker on to a glass. 'That's if they're all different. And what did they cost?'

Poor Mary! She had quite forgotten the price of those markers, and could only remember that the price of one was an exact number of cents less than the price of a tumbler. Maybe you can answer her husband's question.

5. The Model

Her figure's modern, Diorvine—
So slim, you'd say she wears a nine.
Her hips have slipped, her bust's no more:
No more a shapely thirty-four.
Her dresses show the new long torso—
They're *à la mode* and even more so.
Divide her weight in pounds by seven,
And just for fun then add eleven:
Now multiply by one one three,
When three one something four you'll see.
In Sally's weight we disregard
The ounces, so it won't be hard
To ascertain what she must weigh:
Your fun with figures for today!

6. The Wheels of Commerce

'How's the motor business?' asked Bob, glancing at the menu.

Ben owns a used car lot. His cars are good; his prices are right; his guarantee means just what it says. Other dealers come and go, but Ben keeps right on selling. 'Not too bright around Christmas,' he replied, 'but sales have picked up again.'

'That's dandy!' commented Bob. 'I was talking to Stan Logan down on Wardie and Myrtle yesterday. He's hardly sold a car this year.'

Ben smiled. 'A lot of them are having a tough time,' he said, 'but maybe I'm lucky. We've done well so far this month—each week more sales than the previous week.'

'What's that in actual numbers?' asked Bob, who's a great one for facts.

'I'm not sure about the last few days,' replied Ben, 'but we sold fifty-six cars the first three weeks. And here's something to amuse yourself with.' He thought a moment. 'The difference between the numbers we sold in the first and second weeks, multiplied by the difference between the second and third weeks, comes to the same as the number we sold the first week.'

The shapely waitress leaned over his friend just then to take their order, and Bob rather lost interest in car sales. But how many cars would you say Ben sold in the third week?

7. Bill, Bert, and Betty

If Bill were as old as Bert would be if he was as old as Betty's age added to what Bill's age would be if he were twice as old as Bert would be if he were eleven years younger than Bill would be if he were seven years older, he would be twelve years older than the difference between his and Bert's ages.

There's more than ten years between those two, and their ages add up to Betty's age.

So how old does that make Bill?

8. To Watch or Not to Watch

At a meeting of the Society for the Prevention of Cruelty to TV Parents, it was noted that the men out-numbered the women by the number of married couples present. Among those who attended, there were some who had not yet qualified for membership, though they viewed the activities of the Society with sympathetic interest.

There were twenty-six people at the meeting, the bachelors numbering five more than the married men and the spinsters three fewer than the married women.

Our correspondent fails to report the exact number of women who attended, but you will be able to figure it out yourself.

9. The Long Road Home

Beryl opened her eyes. 'I must have been asleep,' she said, yawning luxuriously as she snuggled closer to her husband.

Sam chuckled. 'You've been snoring plenty,' he told her, 'but we're still on the highway.' He indicated a signpost they were approaching. 'That'll tell how far we've still got to go.'

Beryl looked, and yawned again. 'I can't keep my peepers open,' she said, 'but call me if you get bored.'

Two hours later Sam nudged her. 'Wakey, wakey!' he laughed. 'We're passing another signpost and it's time to be sociable.' And now the time did pass quickly, with Beryl doing most of the talking as Sam concentrated on his driving.

Then suddenly she pointed. 'That's funny, Sam!' She was serious a moment. 'The signpost we passed when I woke up the first time had the same two figures as this one, but the other way round.'

Sam smiled. Two could play at that game. 'That's so,' he agreed, 'but you've forgotten there was a third figure between them the first time. And when I called you an hour ago we were just passing one that showed those same two figures but with a nought between them.'

He might have added that he had been driving at a steady speed for well over three hours, but you'll be able to figure out what that speed was.

10. I've Got a Winner

Only three starters lined up for the second race, but they were all well fancied. Mike, who has been known to pick a winner, was quite confident. 'Fay's Folly must win,' he told his friends as they waited for the gate.

Steve wasn't so sure. 'Anyway,' he said 'she won't finish second.'

Stan had been studying his card trying to decide between Kimono and Satan. 'I put Satan in the first two,' he declared.

And then they were off, and Kimono opened a two-length lead hitting out of the gate but soon tired when her jockey went to the whip. It was a thrilling race right up to the finish, being won by only a short head and with less than a length between second and third.

Only one of the three friends had been a true prophet, however. So maybe you can figure out the final placing.

11. Grannie's Age

Ron was trying to guess his grandmother's age. 'The two figures of my age,' she told him, 'are the ages of your cousins Fred and Frank.'

'But I don't know them either,' objected the boy.

'Well, then,' said the old lady, 'if you add together their ages and mine, you get a total of eighty-three.'

It seemed quite impossible. But Ron did manage to work it out. What do you make her age?

12. So Unobservant

'There's something very wrong with Tick-Tock,' observed Gwen, refilling her husband's cup.

John glanced at the fine old grandfather clock in surprise. 'It never gains or loses a minute,' he said. 'What's wrong with it?'

Gwen laughed. 'You never notice things at home, not even me!' she teased. 'The minute hand is always seven minutes past the hour when the hour hand is exactly on the hour.'

'Okay. I'll fix it this evening,' promised John. 'No time now, as it's well past eight and I must be down town by nine.'

At that very moment the two hands were precisely over one another. So what was the time by the hour hand?

13. Just Some Coins

Uncle Frank is generous, but he makes the kids work for their tips. Last time he came he had a new idea for not mixing up his change.

'I keep the cents and nickels in my left pocket,' he told the children, 'and the quarters and dimes in my right.' The kids half guessed what was to follow, and he didn't disappoint them. 'Today I've got as many nickels as cents, and as much in dimes as in quarters,' he went on, 'and altogether I've got two dollars forty-two in those coins.'

Pete was the first to say how many nickels his uncle had, and so he was duly rewarded. How many would you say?

14. A Star Was Born

Passing through the room, George stopped a while to watch his son playing. The boy had a heap of counters beside him, round and shiny and all the same size. And he'd laid out seven of them to form a compact little six-sided star on the polished floor.

'I'm going to make a huge one,' said Pete, and his father went on his way with a smile. When he came back, Pete was still on the floor but with his huge star complete: and he'd made it right, six-sided and regular, with the colours arranged in an attractive design.

'You're quite an artist,' commented George, 'but I didn't know we had that many counters.' Making a quick estimate, he went on: 'There must be between four and five hundred in your star!' And he wasn't wrong.

How many counters had Pete used?

15. Share and Share Alike

'What say we split it even?' suggested Joe, taking the check from the waitress. He glanced at the total. 'I'll pay an extra fifteen cents that way and don't you forget it.'

Jack looked at the check. 'That's O.K. by me,' he laughed, 'as it'll save me twenty-one cents.' He turned to Tom, the other member of their little party. 'And what you had would have cost you a dollar sixty-five, so you don't lose much.'

But you'll have to figure out the total amount.

16. *Twice in a Day*

Professor Brayne suddenly looked up from his writing. 'Did you ask me for the Copes' telephone number, my dear?'

His wife flashed him an affectionate smile. 'That was the best part of an hour ago,' she said. 'But I still want it.' She wouldn't have him different, however. On one occasion she tied a thread around his thumb as a reminder to have his hair cut. Later that day he went to the barber and showed him the thread. 'But I've cut it once already today!' cried the barber.

The professor peered at his wife over his glasses. 'There was a seven or an eight in it,' he told her, 'but I've forgotten the number.' Four little figures can be so elusive. 'But of course! It was the square of its last two figures,' he said triumphantly, thinking aloud.

That was little help to Mrs Brayne, but then her husband worked it out in his head. So what was the number?

17. *Served Him Right!*

Uncle Ken had sent Jack some stamps to share with his sister. The boy counted them and then passed some over to Jill. 'There's about a hundred altogether,' he said, 'and that's your share.'

'You cheat!' cried Jill angrily. 'That's not nearly fifty.'

Jack said nothing. He quietly gave her a fifth of his share, hoping she'd be satisfied. A moment later, however, he regretted doing so. 'Look!' he exclaimed, as if it were her fault. 'Eight of mine are torn.'

'Serves you right,' rejoined Jill, 'and anyway that still leaves you six good ones to every five of mine.'

How many stamps did Jill get?

18. Boy or Girl?

Bob and Betty are a happy couple. She's busy knitting and he's just waiting.

When Bob will be one third of Betty's age older, she will be half his present age younger than he will be three years after that, but when she is a third of his present age older he will be a third of her present age older than she will be eight years after that.

They've decided to name the new arrival John: that's how sure they are. But how old do you make Bob?

19. On Parade

It was raining hard. No holiday weather this! But Tim seemed happy, sitting there on the floor with lead soldiers strewn around him. 'Busy?' asked his father, itching to join in the fun.

'I want to form them up on parade with the same number in each line,' replied the boy. 'I've tried two deep, three deep, and everything up to seven deep, but there's always just one too few.'

'What about the guy in charge?' Tim's father laughed. 'If you stick one of them out in front by himself, you'll be able to form up the rest of them eleven deep.' There were less than five hundred soldiers there, but he must have known exactly how many.

Can you figure out the exact number?

20. *Sharing the Loot*

'It's lucky we aren't one fewer,' said Len, as he finished sharing out the pennies the children had found in the old money box, 'as that would have left a penny over.'

'But we'd each have got a nickel more,' Tom reminded him, grabbing his share.

'So we're still lucky,' insisted Len. 'If there'd been one more of us we'd each have had four cents less and there'd have been two cents over.'

That seemed to settle it, and anyway they shared the loot equally with no argument about odd coins. How many children were there in that share-out?

21. *Only One There*

'Stop it!' cried Ken's mother. 'Your dirty hands all over my nice new handkerchiefs!'

The boy had seized the parcel as soon as she came in and was spreading out her purchases on the table. 'But there's only one handkerchief here, Mum,' he said, holding it up for her to see.

Poor Mrs Brown! And after all the trouble she'd taken to find them. 'You go down to Denson's, Ken,' she told him. 'They'll remember: I got big ones for you at thirty-nine cents and smaller ones like that for Pam at twenty-nine.'

Ken made for the door but stopped with his hand on the knob.

'How many did you get?'

His mother was far too upset to remember that important detail, however. She only knew that the handkerchiefs had cost her \$3.30 altogether. But can you answer Ken's question?

22. *Coincidences*

'That's a funny coincidence,' exclaimed Ruth, looking up from her typewriter. 'I'm doing our invoice 7849, and the amount is seventy-eight dollars and forty-nine cents.'

Harry smiled. 'That wouldn't happen often,' he agreed, 'but it's even funnier that today's the nineteenth.'

Seeing the puzzled look on her face, he explained: 'Just write down your invoice number, but with two very ordinary mathematical signs in the proper places, and you'll get an expression that makes nineteen.'

What do *you* think he meant?

23. *Going Up!*

Everybody knows Len. He's been running that elevator for years. You'd think he'd be bored—up and down, day after day and year after year. But he's always ready with a smile, and maybe a joke if he knows you. They're all his friends on Spadina.

And Len does notice things, and he passes the time figuring out facts in connection with his job: 'statistics', he calls it.

He told Charlie, for example, that out of the first hundred people who'd ridden on his elevator that day, twice the number of girls who went up would have been three less than five times all his other passengers up and down in that period. 'Not counting old Len, stuck here in his pen,' he added in his whimsical way.

So now you can figure out how many girls he *had* taken up.

14

24. Five Minutes is Par

Each letter stands for a different figure, and you will only need common-sense to find the value of THAT.

```
B E T ) T H A T ( O N
        T E N
        -----
        B E T
        B E T
        -----
        - - -
```

25. Something Forgotten

Tim and Tom are near neighbours. They live on the same side of a quiet road—a friendly road with attractive little houses set back in tidy gardens, even numbers one side and odd numbers the other.

The boys go to the same school and are lucky in having a teacher with ideas of his own on the teaching of math and other dull subjects. Encouraged by him, the boys often make up little teasers on things they notice at home. One day Tim produced this for his teacher:

'Multiply the number of my house by itself and then take away the number of houses on our street,' he told the poor man, 'and you'll get the number of Tom's house multiplied by one less than the number of mine.'

The teacher was completely defeated that time: he couldn't know that there are a hundred and thirteen houses on Tim's street. But what do *you* make those two numbers?

26. Miles and Miles and Miles

Dan drove as many miles as the number of minutes he'd have
taken to drive two-thirds of the distance if he'd driven ten
miles an hour faster than he'd have had to drive to drive the
distance he did in ten minutes less than he took, but if he'd
driven half as fast again for ten minutes longer than he did
drive, he'd have driven sixteen miles more than he did.

He contrived to drive at a steady speed, but you'll have to
find out what it was.

27. Fair for All

'Yes, that's our policy,' declared Sam, writing out the order.
'The same price whether you buy one or by the dozen.'

'It's a reasonable way of doing business,' agreed his customer, 'and I also like your pricing in even dollars, though
it's unusual.' Mr Glennie was buying for his store just a
few winter suits to complete his stock. 'So that's the lot,' he
said as Sam handed him the form to sign. 'One of the gabardine, twelve of the tweed, and six of the flannel: just the
three styles and you make it nine hundred and ninety-two
dollars altogether.'

Sam nodded. This was a good order. 'And sales tax is
included in the prices, you know.'

But buyers, be they male or be they female, are all femi-
nine in one respect: they change their minds.

'Sorry, Sam,' announced the customer, handing back the
paper, 'but I'm going to switch the quantities. Make it a
dozen of the gabardine, six tweed, and only one of the flannel.'

Sam got busy again with his pencil. 'Okay, Mr Glennie,'
he said after a moment. 'Two weeks delivery and the total's
nine hundred and eighty-five.'

What was the price of that flannel suit?

28. A Tale of a Teller

It had been a terrible day for Frank. From the time the doors opened that morning there'd been one troublesome customer after another. And he hadn't been feeling too good anyway after Bob's party the night before.

Now at last, the bank doors firmly bolted and the tension eased, his one idea was to get away home to bed. But the cash must be checked first. And of course there had to be this shortage!

Poor Frank. His head in a whirl he went through the day's cheques for a start, and there he found the mistake. On one of them, which he'd cashed for a customer, he had paid the cents as dollars and the dollars as cents. And it wasn't a small mistake either, as he'd handed out just one dollar more than twice the proper amount.

The customer must have noticed, but some people are like that. What was the amount of the cheque?

29. The Hand Moves On

If it were seven minutes later than half as many minutes after the hour as it would be if the hour were minutes and it were one minute less than three times that number of minutes after the hour, it would be half again as many minutes as the number of the hour later than it would be if it were three minutes earlier than half as many minutes as it is after the hour.

That's all very well, but we still need to know how many minutes it is after the hour.

30. *When a Boy Grows Up*

'If half of half
　　　my age,' said Kate,
'Were now replaced
　　　by twenty-eight,
'And then the whole
　　　reduced by four,
'You'd make my age
　　　just eighteen more.
'Why, fancy! When
　　　I'm forty-six,
'My age will be
　　　just double Dick's.'
That's what she said,
　　　and he's her son:
So figure out
　　　his age for fun.

31. *It Isn't All Gold That Glitters*

'It's a give-away, folks!' the huckster cried. 'Five bucks for two jumbo jars of my fabulous face-cream, and a solid gold watch for free with every purchase!'

The watches on the stall sparkled in the harsh light of the hissing flares: cheap metal, quite free—of gold! And the women thronged to part with their money.

If each jar had cost him a dime less, and the watches half as much again, he would have made a profit of two dollars on each sale. As it was he made seventy cents better than that.

That's real business. But what do you think the old rogue paid for each watch?

32. A Rush of Work

It's always that way for Bert: for days on end his machines are idle, and then when an order does come in it's a rush job and he's short of operators. And it was like that now. He had the order and he had the machines, but only old Sam had clocked in.

'You'd better start,' said Bert, 'and maybe some of the others will come in soon.'

'Okay, Boss,' replied Sam, switching on the power. 'I guess we'd get through this lot in six hours if all the machines were going.'

But Bert was lucky. Before very long another man clocked in and started work. And gradually, as the long day passed, they all came in until at last every machine was in use.

By some strange chance, almost as if they'd planned it among themselves, the men came in at exactly equal intervals, and each started work without delay. And last of all came Tim O'Hara—unsteady on his feet and bleary-eyed but precisely on time by the schedule—only to be told that the job was just finished and that he could go back to his bottle.

Pete, the last man in before Tim, worked one-ninth as long as Sam on the job. Bert is proud of his plant—his machines are good and he claims they all work at exactly the same speed—and he was proud of his men this day, working as they did without a break. But how long did it take them to do the job?

33. *A Trick That Went Wrong*

'Think of a number,' said Jack. 'Now treble it.'

Jill's fingers were working hard and she nodded.

'Now take away four times the reverse of the number you first thought of,' the boy continued confidently.

'You mean the two figures the other way round?' queried his sister, grabbing a pencil. She scribbled for a moment, ignoring his sarcastic reply, and then looked up triumphantly. 'I get eight.'

And then Jack found he couldn't find her original number after all. Can you get it?

34. *Such a Tease*

Ken knows very well that his mother has no head for figures, so the little devil rarely misses a chance of teasing her. He came home one day with some cookies he'd been sent to buy. 'Here you are, Mum,' he said, handing her the bag. 'I got five of one sort and twelve of the other.'

His mother examined his purchase. 'That's fine,' she commented, 'but was there much difference in price?'

'Less than a dime,' replied the boy, well prepared for such a question. 'If one sort had cost one cent each less and I'd got one more of them, and if the other sort had cost one cent each more and I'd got one less of them, I'd have spent a nickel less.'

So the poor lady still doesn't know what that difference was. What do *you* make it?

35. *Not So Easy*

Some alphametics can be very deceptive. This one, for example, seems simple enough with its slight suggestion of spring. Each letter stands for a different figure, and you *can* find the meaning of NEST.

```
    S  E  E  S
             A
  ─────────────
    N  E  S  T
```

36. *So Far Across the Seas*

'Was it your great-grandfather came across from the Old Country?' asked Steve.

Mike smiled. 'It was long before his time that the first McFeat landed here,' he said, his voice still holding a hint of that soft brogue that charms colleens the world over, 'but I've got the old Bible he brought with him and the date is written there.'

'When was it, then?' Steve inquired.

'You boast you do "Fun with Figures" every day, so now you can figure it out,' chuckled Mike, whose only interest in figures lies in a very different direction. 'Take the last figure of the year and multiply by ten, and then add a number less than ten.'

'Which year?' Steve interrupted his friend.

'We're talking about the year my venerable ancestor landed,' Mike reminded him. 'Do what I said, and then multiply the result by itself and you'll get back to that fateful year again.'

It was certainly a teaser, even for Steve. What do you make of it?

37. So Good for Him

Ken likes oranges. If you suggested that they might be good for him he'd quickly lose his liking for the fruit, and his parents realize this. Not long ago he walked into the kitchen one morning and showed his mother what he'd just bought. 'It was my own money, Mum!' he reminded her.

'I didn't say anything, dear,' she replied, 'but I guess you paid a lot for so many.'

Even a couple of dozen wouldn't be a lot in Ken's eyes, and he hadn't bought as many as that. 'They cost only seventy cents more than the number of cents you'd get by dividing the number I bought by the price of each,' the boy told her, knowing very well she'd never figure it out.

But maybe you know what Ken paid.

38. It's 'That Man'

'It's nice, isn't it?' simpered Rose. 'You'd never guess their ages.'

She was showing Ruth some snapshots, and the girl had noticed a very good one of two men. 'If this man, whose mother is my mother's mother-in-law, were three years younger than twice as old as that man is,' continued Rose, 'this man would be half as old as he'd be if that man were forty-two.'

She might have added that the ages of the two totalled just ninety years, but even then it would have been too much for Ruth. Maybe you can identify 'that man'. Can you say how old he was?

39. *Other Ages, Other Thrills*

Only a few people patronized the Tattooed Lady at the midway. Maybe they weren't interested in such an old-fashioned show: maybe they were put off by the entrance fee—fifty cents for men, thirty cents for women, and only fifteen cents for children. Anyway, the takings came to only twelve dollars and seventy cents, which barely paid expenses for the day.

If there had been one man less and one woman more among the viewers there would have been twice as many women as men—a surprising thing, considering the type of show. There were some children, of course. If there had been three fewer of them and three more men, the children would have numbered half the men.

So how many people saw the show?

40. *Heads and Tails*

'You take everything that's tails,' said Jack, tossing some coins on the table, 'and I'll keep the heads.'

Jill is smart. There must have been nearly a couple of dozen pennies on the table, but she noticed that all the coins were pennies or nickels. And she noticed more than that. 'Aren't you generous?' she sneered. 'Three-quarters of them are heads.'

But her brother had also checked. 'So what?' he rejoined. 'All but three of the heads are pennies.'

This was indeed true, but Jill wasn't really satisfied until she saw that her share was worth exactly the same as his. So what *was* her share?

23

41. The Eternal Triangle

Old Mr Black is eccentric, but he's rich and people try to humour him. Recently he called on a local realtor and said he wanted to buy a building lot. The agent nodded happily and started turning over some listings, but Mr Black added that he required something rather special. 'It must be triangular,' he declared, 'with one corner a right-angle.'

'Of course!' agreed Mr Kemnitz, showing no surprise.

'The area in square feet must be exactly ten times the perimeter in feet,' continued the old gentleman imperturbably, 'and I won't waste money on fencing, so the perimeter must be less than eighty yards.'

This was too much for the agent. 'Maybe you want each side to be an exact number of feet,' he suggested.

But the sarcasm was wasted on Mr Black. 'That's just what I was going to tell you,' he replied, reaching for his hat.

Mr Kemnitz did find exactly what his client required and at a price that was, for himself at least, most satisfactory. So what were the dimensions of the lot?

42. A Family Argument

'Here's a card from the Morgans,' said John, coming in from the hall with the mail. 'We haven't heard from them for ages.'

'Tom was never much of a writer,' commented Ruth, 'and I guess Ann's too busy with the kids.'

John nodded. 'I guess so. They've got four, as far as I recall—two boys and two girls.'

'Give them a chance,' laughed his wife. 'You may hear news of them at the office, but I'm sure it's only two, a boy and a girl.'

Pam now joined in the discussion. After all, Peggy Morgan had been her best friend before they'd all gone out west. 'I haven't heard from Peg since she left,' she said, 'but somebody at school has heard. She's now got two brothers, so there are three kids in the family.'

As a matter of fact they were all partly right and partly wrong. Among them, the correct number of boys and the correct number of girls had been mentioned, and also the correct total of the Morgan children. But each of the three had made only one correct statement about the composition of that family.

Could you say how many brothers Peggy Morgan had?

43. Thirty-nine Steps

'What in heck are you doing?' called Mrs Brent, hearing the noise on the stairs.

'Getting exercise,' replied Tim who had just reached the top. 'I came up three steps at a time, but each time I went down two steps.'

'There's no sense in that—up three and down two, just to mount one,' commented his mother, turning again to her book.

'But Dad says I need exercise,' the boy reminded her. 'That way I climbed thirty-nine steps altogether to reach the top.'

So now you'll know how many steps there were in that staircase.

44. Eggs and Eggs

'These are our best eggs, Mrs Green,' said the girl. 'We've got smaller ones at fifty-five cents, but these are sixty-five a dozen.'

'I'll take some of each, then,' the old lady decided, 'so give me a dollar eighty's worth.'

There was much muttering and scribbling behind the counter, but no sign of any result. 'All right,' cried Mrs Green at last, 'just give me as many eggs as you can at those prices, but keep it to the dollar eighty.'

And then the girl did manage to figure something out. So how many eggs did Mrs Green get?

45. A Bicycle Made for Two

What's the idea of a tandem? Peter would say: 'Pedal, park awhile, then pedal some more.'

He and Pam went off for a long jaunt on Easter Sunday. Pedalling alone, Peter made a steady 12 miles an hour, and kept it up for a fifth of the total distance they rode. Pam also did some solo pedalling, but was only able to manage a speed of 10 miles an hour; she did this for a fifth of the total time they were cycling.

Most of the way they pedalled together at a good average speed of 15 miles an hour—for twenty-six miles, in fact.

It might be tactless to ask how far they went, but maybe you can guess.

46. An Easy Alphametic

This isn't quite such nonsense as you might think. Each letter stands for a different figure, and you won't find it hard to get the meaning of BONE.

```
N O ) B O N E ( B E
      W E E
      ─────
        E V E
        D O E
        ─────
          M A
```

47. *It Was Spring Again*

Jake started saving when he got married in January 1952. He stowed away a number of one-dollar bills in his old iron box (Jake doesn't believe in banks). The following July he again put a wad of one-dollar bills into the box. Each succeeding January he added half as much again as he had stowed away the previous January, and each succeeding July half as much again as the previous July.

Jake is a real country lad, careful and thrifty—it never occurred to him to draw on his precious secret hoard. But there came a day, early in 1957, when spring was in the air and Janet said something about a car. And Jake smiled happily as he told her the surprising news. 'We'll buy one right now,' he said.

'But how?' exclaimed Janet, not daring to believe. 'You know we haven't the money.'

'Oh, yes we have!' he replied proudly. 'I've saved up twenty-three hundred and forty bucks and twenty-five cents.'

It was so like him to remember the odd quarter and that made Janet smile. But Jake knew to a penny how much he had accumulated in that old box.

How much had he stowed away when he married Janet?

48. A Lady Loses

'No more for me!' exclaimed Jill, putting the cards away. 'I've lost two games out of three and you've won thirty-two cents.'

Jack didn't really mind: he'd made a good profit. 'All right, meanie,' he said, 'but you started with nearly a dollar. It's funny the way the scoring went.'

'Not to me,' rejoined his sister, who hates losing money and doesn't like cards anyway. 'What was funny about it?'

'Maybe "strange",' Jack admitted. 'The first game you lost a quarter of what you had, and the second game you won a quarter of what I had then, and the last game you lost a quarter of what you had left.'

And so it was, but you'll be able to figure out how much Jack had when they started.

49. Gentlemen Don't Ask

'How old's Grandma?' asked Ted, looking at the photo on the dresser.

'You'll soon be too old to be asking ladies' ages,' laughed his father, 'but you can amuse yourself figuring it out.' He paused (it would never do to get it wrong). 'If you reverse the figures of her age you'll get Aunt Amelia's age, and the difference between their ages is one year less than the age of one of them.'

That kept the boy quiet for a while. But what do you make his grandmother's age?

50. *No Dream of Greatness*

'Last night I had such an odd dream,' remarked Steve. His wife went on with her breakfast, saying nothing. Steve tried again. 'I dreamt you were a midget.'

Other peoples' dreams are so boring, but Mary couldn't let this pass. 'Maybe that's the way you think of me,' she suggested sweetly.

'Of course, my dear,' replied Steve, 'but I was little too.' He took a sip of coffee and continued. 'We were on bicycles riding down a long passage inside the City Hall, and there was a sort of obstruction.'

'That's why they don't get things done, such as fixing our road,' laughed Mary, 'and clearing the garbage in the streets.'

Her husband nodded. 'But it wasn't trash: only two straight poles barred the way.'

'Couldn't we ride between them then?' Mary showed dutiful interest.

'No,' said Steve. 'One was a hundred and five inches long, the other ninety-one inches; and they were placed crosswise from the foot of each wall, square across to the opposite wall and crossing near the middle.' He paused a moment. 'That was odd too. I knew those lengths exactly, and that the passage was just seven feet wide.'

Mary stifled a yawn. 'And what happened?'

'Well,' concluded her husband. 'I knew to a fraction of an inch how high the cross of the two poles was. So we dismounted and walked under.'

Of course it was only a silly dream and so Steve would not have bothered about such a detail as the thickness of the poles. But it would be interesting to know that height.

51. When Dad's Away

'Coming, Mum!' answered Ken when called down to dinner. But minutes passed and still the boy did not appear. His mother waited impatiently, wishing she could be firm like some of her friends. 'It happens every time his Dad's away,' she sighed.

When he did deign to come down from what he calls his 'study', Ken seemed more interested in a scrap of paper than in the steaming bowl of onion soup that was set before him. 'I've figured out something about our ages,' he remarked blandly, referring to his brother and younger sister. 'If you multiply my age by itself and add that to three times Peg's age multiplied by itself, you get John's age multiplied by itself.'

His mother made no comment. She was trying to remember if John, her nineteen-year-old boy, had been at all that way when he was Ken's age. And what age would *that* be?

52. Like Sheep

Mike says women are like sheep. 'Look at them!' he jeers. 'Women in uniform, all wearing the same clothes.' And there's really something in what he says, with cheap garments being mass-produced these days.

'You're right, you know,' said his wife one day as a bulky female brushed past them on Bloor Street. 'I don't know how many times we've passed that same coat today.'

Mike grinned. He'd been checking them himself. 'Less than a hundred,' he told Betty, 'but there'll be more. If they'd been grouped in pairs there'd have been one over, if in threes two over, if in fours three over, and if in fives four over.'

That wasn't quite what she expected, but Betty did manage to figure out the total number. Could you?

53. *One Way with a Secret*

'How old's your mother?' asked Gwen, finding that her new friend was the same age as herself.

'It's really a secret,' replied Ann, 'but Mum is older than you'd think.'

Gwen was curious. 'Come on,' she pleaded. 'I won't tell.'

'Okay,' said Ann after a moment's thought, 'but you can't say I told you. Mum is seven years younger than Dad, and her age and mine come to nine-tenths of mine and Dad's, and four years ago our three ages added up to ten times what I am now.'

Ann hadn't actually 'told', of course. But can *you* find her mother's age?

54. *In the Fall*

'We're through, Mum!' announced Pam, coming into the kitchen with her brother.

Pete laughed. 'Listen to her,' he jeered. 'She says "we" when she'd have taken five hours longer to clear all those leaves by herself.'

Pam turned on him angrily. 'Anyway you were glad to have us help you, and you'd have taken twice as long yourself.'

'That's enough,' their mother told them. 'Wash your hands and we'll have tea.'

But Pete wasn't ready to let the matter drop. 'Tom helped us,' he said, 'and that was real help.' He made a face at his sister. 'Without dear Pam's assistance we would have cleared the lot in twelve minutes longer than the three of us took, so you see what little help she was.'

It all sounded very complicated, but we must assume that the children were right in what they said. And then you'll want to know just how long it had taken the three of them to clear those leaves.

55. If At First You Don't Succeed . . .

You'll be lucky if you manage to do this in five minutes. But it is only simple arithmetic involving addition and subtraction.

Write down the numbers 1 through 9 in their proper order but leaving spaces between them. Then put in one plus sign and three minus signs, a sign in each of four spaces, so as to get a total of 88.

It sounds simple enough. But try it.

56. Figures, Just Figures

You needn't fear
Odd fractions here,
For they'd be quite absurd.
My first take thrice,
My second twice,
And add them to my third.
And then, I say,
Take nine away
And multiply by three.
So that's the lot,
For now you've got
A hundred less than me.
But what am I?
You'll have to try:
That's if you want some fun.
Unless I'm wrong
You won't take long
To figure how it's done.

57. *Good and Cold*

The boys came back home with smeary faces and ice-cream cones in their hands. 'So that's how you waste your money,' their mother scolded, 'and to be seen out like that!'

'But we've all still got something left,' said Tom. 'If Tim gave Tam six cents, he'd have half as much as Tam.'

'That's right,' agreed Tim, 'and if Tam gave Tom six cents he'd have half as much as Tom.'

Tam had to have his say. 'But if Tom gave Tim six cents,' he told her, 'they'd both have the same amount.'

Poor Mrs O'Rorke! She couldn't make head or tail of such nonsense. Maybe you can?

58. *Tomorrow on Tuesday*

'I'll be thirteen next week,' said John when asked his age, 'when tomorrow on Tuesday is yesterday.'

But Mrs Bryce is smarter than she looks. 'Then you're as many years older than my Jack as he would be years older than you if he were three years younger than twice as old as you would be if you were three years younger than twice as many years old as the number of days your birthday is after his.'

She paused for breath and then went on. 'And of course his birthday will be this week when yesterday on Sunday is tomorrow.'

That wiped the grin off John's face. But how old was Jack going to be that week?

59. Miaow! Miaow!

Rose and Muriel are neighbours, and each is the proud mother of triplets. 'It's funny about the ages of my three,' remarked Rose one day as they gossiped across the fence. 'If you multiply them together and then add what you get by doing the same with the ages of your three, you get twenty-five hundred and forty. That's my age, twenty-five, followed by yours.'

Muriel makes no bones about her age but she couldn't let this pass. 'Yes,' she murmured sweetly, 'and of course it's also very funny about your age.'

So what do you make the ages of those children?

60. Watches Want Winding

Jack had heard the church clock strike four, but that seemed an age ago and still there was no sign of the general clearing of desks that always started well before five o'clock. 'What's the time, Jim?' he asked. 'My watch stopped.'

'So you forgot to wind it last night,' laughed his friend. 'I guess it was a good party.' He glanced at his own watch. 'It would be three minutes after a quarter before six if the hour hand were where the minute hand is now.'

Jack figured it out with the help of his watch. But maybe you could do so without that aid.

61. Why the Early Train?

Bill started commuting to work last summer, and Gwen says he'd never go back to the misery of driving into town every morning. Now it's become a regular routine for both of them, brought to a fine art with no time wasted at all.

She drives out from home at the same time every day to meet his train, which arrives at Wyeville station sharp at six o'clock. It's a good road and she always drives the same speed both ways.

But Bill left his office unusually early last Friday and so caught a train that reached Wyeville at 5.16 p.m. It was a fine evening for walking, and he stepped out briskly on the road home. It wasn't long before Gwen met him, of course, and she wasted no time asking questions—she turned and drove him right home.

As they stopped in the driveway Bill looked at his watch. 'Why,' he exclaimed, 'after all that we're only eleven minutes early!'

Gwen smiled, saying nothing. She'd been quite happy driving at her regular speed. Bill had walked at a steady 4 miles an hour from the station, but how fast had Gwen driven?

62. The Boss Smiled

Simple Simon strutted into the boss's office. Having held his job for some weeks he felt very sure of himself. 'You called me, Mr Jenks?' His voice was casual.

Mr Jenks was amused but didn't show it. 'You'll have to do better than this,' he said sternly, pointing to a paper on his desk.

Simon looked and recognized an invoice that he himself had made up and sent out. Now it was scrawled across in red ink, and the words were not polite. 'Not only did you reverse the unit price of the goods, giving the dollars as cents and the cents as dollars, but you charged them for three instead of five,' the boss told him.

'Gee, sir, I'm sorry,' mumbled Simon, his pride quite deflated. 'But it only came to thirteen cents too much.'

Then Mr Jenks did smile. But what should the boy have charged for those five items?

63. When the Mangoes are Ripe

'How do we divide them?' asked Piff, hungry after so much climbing. 'Easy,' said Paff. 'I take my lucky number,' he counted out some mangoes from the heap, 'and then I take a quarter of what remains.'

'And I'll do the same,' chipped in Poff. 'Paff's lucky number and then a quarter of what's left.' He did so, much to the disgust of the other two who waited, afraid to interfere.

But now it was Puff's turn. He also took the big fellow's lucky number and then a quarter of what remained.

Poor little Piff had been very patient. He spread his paws wide, hoping to take most of what remained. But no. 'You take your proper share, same as we did,' Paff chattered angrily.

'Proper for you, all right,' gibbered Piff, but he did as he was told, taking the same lucky number and then a quarter of the rest. And now Paff divided the remaining mangoes equally among the four of them, and so Piff was able to start his supper.

The four monkeys had collected a lot of the fruit, but can you figure out the smallest number Piff could have had as his total share?

64. Just a Scrap of Paper

Peter went off with a bulging wallet to buy a quantity of identical articles for himself and his six colleagues in the office.

He returned with the goods which they divided equally among them, but his only record of the purchase was on a crumpled scrap of paper that he still had in his pocket. He had checked the girl's multiplication, in cents to be on the safe side, but most of his figures were illegible. The figures that could be read are shown below, the others being indicated by x's. How many of those articles did Peter buy?

$$
\begin{array}{r}
\text{x x 5} \\
\text{4 x} \\
\hline
\text{3 x x} \\
\text{x 2 x x} \\
\hline
\text{1 x x x x}
\end{array}
$$

65. A Boy Goes Shopping

Kim likes cookies, and his mother sent him out to buy some. 'Get two dozen,' she said, but the boy brought back thirty one. 'You never do what you're told,' she scolded, not really angry as she likes them too.

'They were so cheap, Mum,' replied Kim, 'and I spent only eleven cents more than the three bucks you gave me, and they're three different kinds.' He picked a macaroon and took a bite. 'These cost as many cents each as the number of nut slices I got, and they cost as many cents each as the number of cream squares.'

The boy paused to make sure she was listening. 'And the funny thing is that the cream squares cost as many cents each as the number of macaroons I got.'

'Well, I see nothing very funny about it, but they're good,' laughed his mother, completely mollified. So what were the prices of those cookies?

66. Fast or Slow

'I really must get my watch fixed,' said Ted, glancing down at his wrist. 'It's gained a lot since yesterday.'

'Mine too,' said Molly. 'It shows four minutes after eight.'

'That's as much out as mine has gained,' commented her husband, reaching for the marmalade.

Meanwhile the children had been checking their own watches. 'Mine showed twenty after eight, and Peg's eight-thirteen,' declared Ron.

Ted smiled. This was like a game. 'Your watch is as much wrong as a third, and Peg's as much as a quarter of what mine has gained,' he informed the boy, 'and now you can figure out what that gain is.'

Can *you* do so?

67. Her Three Men

'It's a lovely photo—my three men,' exclaimed Mary, peering over her husband's shoulder. The little group certainly made a fine picture—her father in the middle, amazingly young for his years, with her husband on one side and her son on the other.

Jack wasn't interested in family groups, however. He had just figured out something far more important. 'D'you know something funny about our ages five years ago, Mum?' he called from across the room. 'If you reverse Grandpa's age you get three times Dad's age, and Grandpa is as much older than Dad as my age five years ago multiplied by itself.'

His father looked around. 'Smart, but badly worded!' he commented. 'You mean complete years without odd months.'

Jack's father was right. So how old was Jack at the time of this incident?

41

68. An Old-timer

'Well, if it isn't Len after all these years,' cried Jim as an ancient automobile drew in to the curb. 'And still with the same old jalopy!'

His friend stepped out to a medley of creaks and squeaks. 'But it's had a new engine since you saw me last,' he said, holding out his hand. 'In a year's time it will be four times as old as the engine, and then I'll trade it in for a new car.'

Jim laughed. 'I've forgotten when you bought it,' he said, 'but it might do for a museum.'

'Okay, Jim,' replied Len. 'You always liked teasers. When the car was seven times as old as the engine it was four-and-a-half times as old as the engine is now.'

That was quite enough for Jim. But how old was the car?

69. Quite a Library

When John and Jane were wed, one present was a large desk with a glassed-in bookcase on top. A fine piece, it would have been most useful if they had had any books. So Jane's father came to the rescue. Pulling a steel measuring tape from his pocket he jotted down some figures. A few moments later he hurried out of the little apartment with the enigmatic remark: 'Anyway I'll enjoy them, even if you don't read.'

Some days later a huge crate of books arrived, and Jane spent hours arranging them to fill the bookcase completely. 'Your Dad's a great one for accuracy,' laughed John when he came home that evening, seeing that the books exactly fitted the two sixty-two-inch shelves. They looked good there, neatly graded in sets.

There were books half-an-inch thick, and half that number half again as thick; there were a third as many one-inch thick as half-an-inch; there were massive tomes two inches thick, only a fifth as many as the half-inch volumes, and the collection was rounded off with some dusty two-and-a-half-inch treatises.

It was all very clever of him, of course, but how many books did Jane's father send them?

70. A More Difficult One

You know the rule: each letter stands for a different figure. Then what's the SCORE?

```
O U R ) S C O R E ( U R N
        O U R
        ─────
        C N E R
        C U C C
        ─────────
          U K C E
          U B K V
          ─────────
            K U U
```

71. Pearls at a Price

Pam planned to smarten up her old black bag. It would look cute with some nice bright beads, so she went downtown to Seton's. And there she found just what she wanted: lustrous pearls and sparkling rhinestones. They were more expensive than she had expected, but then that's always the way.

After making her selection, Pam had to wait a while for the young lady behind the counter to finish her conversation with 'Ribbons' across the aisle, and then at last she got attention. 'Pearls are nineteen cents each, and rhinestones twelve cents each,' drawled the assistant, 'so that's two seventy-seven altogether.'

It was plenty to pay for that old bag. But how many pearls did Pam get?

72. The Humorist at Home

Bill seldom misses any chance of teasing his wife who has no head at all for figures. One day her watch had stopped and she asked him the time.

'Three times the number of minutes it's after eight,' replied Bill, enjoying his joke, 'is five more than twice the number of minutes still to go before ten o'clock.'

With that the poor girl had to be content. But what do you make of it?

73. Tell Me True

'Now tell me, little Freddie,' said
               his teacher Mrs Drew,
'As nine times these and five times those
               add up to eighty-two,
'How many altogether would
               I have if half of these
'And one of those were thrown away?
               Just tell me, if you please.'

74. A Man Decides

George looked stern as he sat down to breakfast. His wife paid no attention to this, however. She chattered away blithely about this and that, giving him no chance to start the row that seemed to threaten.

At last Helen came to the inevitable topic of conversation, remarking how mild it was for the first half of March. And her husband seized the opportunity for which he had waited so grimly.

'That reminds me, dear,' he told her. 'I've made a decision. For the rest of the month I'm cutting down on my smokes.'

So that's what he'd had on his mind! Helen smiled. She had heard it so often before.

'Starting today,' continued George, 'I'll smoke only thirteen cigarettes a day, but only three every third day, and right to the end of the month at that.'

This seemed needlessly complicated to Helen. 'Why don't you just smoke ten a day right through?' she ventured. 'It would come to the same thing.'

She was right of course. But what was the date when this conversation took place?

75. At the Drug Store

Stopping in at a drug store just off Yonge Street, I sat down at the short counter on the fourth stool from the end. The last three places were already occupied by three young men who seemed to have struck up a casual acquaintance while they ate. Young and uninhibited, they conversed in loud voices for all to hear, so it was not long before I felt I knew quite a lot about them. And so was born an idea.

The young men answered to the names Jack, Jim, and Joe. One was a salesman, one a clerk, and one an artist. One drank milk, one sipped coffee, and one refreshed himself with tea.

The salesman sat next to Jack, and Jim's neighbour was drinking tea. The artist sat next to the milk drinker. The clerk was not drinking coffee and Jack was not drinking milk.

As I finished my sandwich, the artist offered Joe a cigarette and then insisted on paying for all three of them.

So, having noted those few details, I wonder if you can say which of the three sat in the middle, and also give his occupation and what he was drinking.

76. Cats and Canaries

Ken was very quiet when he returned from his stay with Aunt Arabella—so quiet that his father asked if he was sick.

'I'm fine,' replied the boy, 'but it's so good to be away from that mad-house.' He explained that his aunt's place was full of pets. He had seen no dogs, and not even an occasional visitor—just Aunt Arabella and her canaries and her cats.

'Yes, I know. But she's very fond of you, and that may mean a lot one day,' commented his father. 'How many pets has she got now?'

Ken could answer that after ten long days there. 'They have five times as many legs among them as there are canaries,' he said, 'and that's fifty-one legs more than the number of cats.'

So how many cats did Aunt Arabella have?

77. So Many Buttons

Jill was on the floor with the contents of her mother's workbasket strewn around her. 'I'm tidying it for you,' she said when her mother came into the room.

The buttons bothered Jill. She wanted to arrange them in equal lots, but it wasn't easy. She had tried them in fours but there was one too many; going to the other extreme she had tried by the dozen, but had five buttons over that way.

'Have you got three more buttons some place, Mum?' she asked. 'Then I can divide them into tens.'

Jill's mother wasn't going to waste time searching, but she did solve the child's problem with the buttons that were there.

There were less than a hundred of them, but what was the exact number?

78. What's What?

Take five times which
          plus half of what,
And make the square
          of what you've got.
Divide by one-
          and-thirty square,
To get just four—
          that's right, it's there.
Now two more points
          I must impress:
Both which and what
          are fractionless,
And what less which
          is not a lot:
Just two or three.
          So now what's what?

79. A Fishy Tale

The cars stopped and the men tumbled out, impatient to start on the river that rippled so invitingly close at hand. As they put up their rods an idea struck Harry. 'There's nearly a mile of water,' he said, 'so let's draw lots and each take a two-hundred-yard stretch.'

This was agreed upon and soon arranged. But then Bert took a quick look upstream. 'My beat's all bushes,' he complained, 'and I'll never get my fly on the water.'

'Okay,' laughed Harry, never at a loss. 'Then we'll all pool what we catch and share equally.' Nobody objected to this, and so the fishing started.

At the end of the day the anglers gathered at the cars and unhitched their baskets. They all laughed when Bert tipped out a big catch of rather small trout—the trees hadn't bothered him that much. The next man added to Bert's heap one more than half as many fish as Bert had caught, the third man two more than half the second man's contribution, the fourth three more than half the third's, and so on—it just happened that way.

But it was even more extraordinary that they were able to divide the total catch evenly just as Harry had suggested, each getting two dozen fish.

So how many fishermen were there?

80. Curiosity Rewarded

It was raining hard and Ron was amusing himself looking through an old scrapbook of his mother's. 'Look, Dad,' he said suddenly. 'Here's a photo of Grandpa dated 1899. He must be very old now.'

His father smiled, doing a quick calculation in his head. 'He'd have been about your age then,' he told the boy, 'but you can figure it out yourself. Reverse the figures of the difference between his age and yours, and subtract your grandfather's age and you'll get twenty-two.'

Ron is only in his teens, but he did figure it out. How old do you make his grandfather?

81. Another Matter of Age

Susan and her brother Sam are little. In fact neither is yet ten years old.

If Sam were one year older than Susan would be if she were half as old as Sam would be if he were two years older than three times the difference between their ages, he would be three years younger than twice as old as he is.

If Susan were one year younger than Sam would be if he were twice as old as Susan would be if she were two years younger than three times the difference between their ages, she would be three years older than twice as old as she is.

So now you'll want to know how old they are.

82. *All the Winners*

Bert came back from the races, morose and dejected. 'What about your famous system?' asked Gwen. 'You look like you'd lost!'

'Well, I did end up three bucks down,' replied her husband, 'but I'd have won plenty if it hadn't been for the last race.'

'So what happened?' Gwen likes to know the details, although she never bets herself.

'The first four races I picked the winner and won the same amount each time,' Bert told her. 'Four hand-outs of good crisp dollars—no petty cents from those races.'

'Funny coincidence,' commented Gwen, 'but you should have stopped then.'

'Easy to say now,' rejoined her husband, 'but that infernal Satan seemed a sure thing for the fifth race and I staked plenty on him, and then he came in last.' He smiled ruefully. 'And maybe that's also a funny thing, as I staked exactly the reverse of what I'd won on each of the previous races.'

Maybe it was lucky that he came home after the fifth race, as Bert is not a wise gambler. And it's a good thing Gwen never knew he'd lost the best part of a thousand dollars on that one race. But you will be able to figure out the exact amount.

83. *They All Looked Alike*

'It doesn't matter about their number,' said Mike as they turned into Myrtle Road. 'We'll remember the house when we see it.'

After a lapse of five years he was being rather optimistic, for all the houses in that road looked drearily alike. 'So now we find a phone and look in the book,' commented Mary after they'd cruised the length of the road.

'And that's easy on a Sunday,' rejoined her husband. 'But wait a minute,' he went on. 'I think I've got it.'

He pulled out his bulky wallet and extracted a faded scrap of paper from its depths. 'Sam's a great one for teasers, you remember, and here's one he gave me that time we came over here. He said it was on the number of their house.'

Mary was past optimism. 'If he didn't write down the answer,' she observed dryly, 'it'll be quicker to find a phone.'

But Mike was already reading. 'Here we are,' he said. 'It's a two-figure number. If you multiply it by its second figure and then subtract the difference between the two figures, you get a hundred times the first figure.'

The answer wasn't there, of course, but Mike did manage to find it. What would you say?

84. How Green is Green?

Garry certainly knows that blue and yellow make green. One day he was busy in the yard when his mother came out. 'Look at your face!' she cried. 'And your clothes!'

'It'll all come off with turps,' replied the boy, 'but I've got to get this green darker for the shed.'

His mother watched for a while. He had two big cans, both nearly full of paint. One, which he said had six quarts in it, held a mixture of a rather light shade; the other contained two quarts of a much darker green. 'I want it between these two shades,' explained Garry.

In each hand he held an old tin mug. Dipping the mugs into the cans simultaneously, he transferred a brimming mug of the darker mixture to the can that held the lighter green and a brimming mug of the lighter paint to the can containing the darker shade. 'I have to do it that way,' he told his mother, 'because there's no room to spare in the cans. And anyhow these old mugs hold the same quantity.'

'You're getting nowhere, Garry,' laughed his mother after watching him make several such transfers. 'The shade doesn't change any more, so you'd best use what you've got.'

It wasn't quite the shade the boy had wanted, but that's often the way when you try mixing paints. How much did those old tin mugs hold?

85. *The Anniversary*

'Dad,' said Fred. 'I know it's this month, but what date is your wedding anniversary?'

His father considered the question a moment. 'We were married in Winnipeg, you know,' he replied. 'A fine summer day like this. This year we'll have been married twice as many years as the day of the month. If you add that day of the month to the number of years and multiply by two and divide by eleven, you'll get the number of this month.'

Fred looked puzzled, as well he might. 'I don't get the last part,' he said.

His father smiled. 'March would be number three,' he said.

It took some figuring out, but Fred won't forget again. What month was his father married, and what day of that month?

86. *Kim's Code*

Miss Prim stopped at Kim's desk. 'Let's see how you're getting on,' she said, picking up the sheet of paper on which he was working. But there was something very wrong about what she saw there:

$$
\begin{array}{cccc}
4 & 7 & 8 & 1 \\
4 & 1 & 4 & 8 \\
\hline
7 & 8 & 1 & 8
\end{array}
$$

'Those aren't the numbers you had to add,' she told him, 'and you've added them wrong anyway.'

Kim grinned. He's very intelligent but has a most annoying sense of humour. 'I did it in code,' he said. And that's just what he *had* done.

What do you make of it?

87. An Ugly Monster

A freak, a most unusual pike,
Was caught at Jackson's Point by Mike.
This fish was ugly, huge and strong,
With head alone twelve inches long.
Its body equalled, so Mike said,
Just half its tail plus twice its head:
A third the monster's total length
Was tail, grotesque but built for strength.
So maybe now you'd like to see
How long this curious fish would be.

88. Fired Again

Simple Simon got a new job selling china in a small store. 'What's the price of these?' asked his first customer, a florid female with a hard face, holding up a cup and saucer.

'They'll cost you a quarter less than one cup and two saucers would cost as two cups and three saucers cost a dollar eighty more than those will cost you,' replied Simon in his most friendly way.

Some customers might have been amused, but not so Mrs Merton. And so now poor Simon's looking for a job again.

What do you make the price of that cup and saucer?

89. *Count the Kalotans*

Kalota may lack washing machines and liquor laws and many other amenities that some of us consider essentials. But those sturdy islanders are healthy and happy, and they do remain individuals scorning the dreary sameness of modern civilization. And those delightful people are by no means dying off. Last year's census showed a further increase, though they still have a long way to go before reaching the half-million mark.

Looking through some old records when he was over there for a short vacation this year, Bob came across an official estimate of population made a hundred years ago. There must have been a great increase since then, as that estimate was exactly a quarter of the total given by last year's census.

But Bob says he also noted a strange coincidence on comparing the numbers. Taking away the final or last figure of that old estimate and tacking it on in front of the first figure but leaving all the other figures the same, he got the actual census total of last year.

If you are really interested you'll be able to figure it out yourself.

90. That's Tom, It Was!

One Monday morning, early but after the heavy traffic of Buffalo weekenders had cleared, Bill and Tom drove along the Queen Elizabeth Highway. Bill was on his way out of Toronto to start a week of selling, while Tom passed him in the opposite direction on his way into the metropolis.

As it happened, each maintained a steady speed for ten minutes or so on either side of eight o'clock.

At exactly three minutes before the hour they were six miles apart, and at two minutes after eight they were a quarter of that distance apart. At one minute before eight, however, they were three miles apart.

Can you figure out the time when they passed each other?

91. The Gold-digger

'How much have you got?' asked Jill, hoping to wheedle some cash out of her brother.

'Let's see what you've got,' replied Jack, 'and then we'll compare.'

Out came all their coins, and by a strange chance the boy had as many nickels as Jill had pennies and as many pennies as Jill had nickels, and that was all they had.

'Okay,' laughed Jack in generous mood that day, 'I'll keep one and give you the rest of my nickels if you'll keep a penny and give me the rest of your pennies.'

Jill found this a very fair exchange, for these transfers left her with sixteen cents more than Jack.

So how many coins did they have altogether?

92. *And a Trip Around the Island*

The parents were as bad as the kids, and Ben seemed glad when the last of his coaches pulled out of the yard full of noisy humanity. 'You fixed a popular excursion this time,' Jim remarked, following him back into the office.

'We get it good sometimes,' his old friend nodded, 'and I'm well satisfied with the hundred tickets we sold for today's outing.' He passed Jim a handbill. 'That's the program.'

Jim glanced at the paper. 'Tour to Toronto', it said, and there followed details of an interesting itinerary. And the charges were reasonable enough: all the way to Sunnyside and back for $3.00, with children half price, and for an extra payment of $2.65 ($2.20 for a child) there was the additional attraction of a trip around the Island with lunch aboard the steamer. 'Not much profit in that,' Jim commented.

'More profit, more tax,' Ben laughed. 'But I've taken exactly four hundred bucks, and I guess that'll cover expenses.'

He did mention that a quarter of the bookings around the Island had been for adults, but he didn't say how many. Maybe *you* can figure out how many tickets he sold for that steamer trip.

93. *What Jack Said*

'Our Betty's age by Sarah's age,
        Plus John's by Jim's, you'll see,
If figured out the proper way
        Will give you three four three.
But Betty's younger than our John
        By just five years, no more:
And added, John's and Betty's years
        Make nine years plus a score.'
Jack told me that, and only that.
        Of course I'm rather slow,
But still I don't know Jimmie's age:
        I wonder if you know?

94. *Cheaper Next Door*

Mrs Green came home in a rage. 'What's biting you?' asked her husband, realizing that something serious must have happened to disturb her customary calm.

'They bilked me over these bananas,' she told him, laying her basket on the table. 'They're for Pam's party tomorrow and I spent two dollars ten on them.' She held up some of the fruit. 'Then right next door I saw the same at one cent a pound cheaper, so for the same money I could have bought one pound more there.'

No wonder Mrs Green was upset. But how many pounds of bananas did she buy?

95. A Second Solomon

Four piggy banks full of cash! Four identical china piggy
banks, but moved from their special places and piled together when the children's play-room was painted. That
was the sad situation as Dad found it when he came home
in the evening.

'Break them open and share the money among you,' he
advised. 'I'll buy you four new ones, but in different colours.'

So the division started. Bob, the eldest, had surely saved
the most: he took one dollar and then a quarter of what
remained. Bill followed: ignoring the protests of his sisters,
he took two dollars and then a quarter of the balance.

Ann came next. She started to divide the heap into two,
but thought better of it: she took three dollars and then a
quarter of what was left.

Peggy grabbed the rest and made for the door, but Bob
stopped that. 'No, you don't!' he cried. 'You take four bucks
and then a quarter of the rest.' Peggy did as she was told,
leaving between six and seven dollars' worth of coins on the
table, and that the four shared out exactly equally.

It would be interesting to know how much there had been
altogether.

96. Do You Get It?

'At the regular price
              for this cute little hat,
'I'd have spent two-thirds more
              and a quarter on that.'
Answered Mary, back home
              from a sale at the store,
'And the hat would have cost
              fifty-eight nickels more.'
When you see just what sort
              of a 'quarter' she meant,
You'll be able to figure
              what Mary had spent.

97. The Fly on the Wall

Lying in his warm bed those last precious moments, Ken noticed a drowsy fly over in the corner of his room. Gladly he seized on the excuse for staying a while longer before rising to face another day. 'Mum can't call me lazy,' he muttered. 'This is like homework.'

That fly was perched a third of the way down from the ceiling, right in the far corner. No spider was in sight, but Ken imagined one almost overhead, close up to the ceiling in the corner diagonally opposite to where the fly rested.

And then he started to figure out how far his spider would have to crawl to reach her prey by the shortest route—a hard mental exercise for any youngster, but what an excuse!

Ken's room is just nine feet square and nine feet from floor to ceiling, so maybe you can solve his problem.

98. And Then Some!

Ron takes a peculiar interest in ages. It's sometimes quite embarrassing for his mother, especially when the boy gets to work on her friends. Yesterday it happened again, though he had been scolded at breakfast for being so rude to Mrs Curtis the previous day.

Mrs Devlin came in for a cup of coffee, and Ron had to blurt out the forbidden question: 'How old are you, please?' Luckily he said nothing about his father's calling her 'That old hag'!

The good lady was not at all put out, however. She'd had much experience of small boys as a teacher years ago. 'Why not figure it out yourself?' she suggested kindly. 'Reverse the figures of my age and multiply that by three, and then you'll see what my age will be in a year's time.

It was too much for Ron. But his father figured it out when he came home, and he only laughed when the boy asked if it made sense. How old would Mrs Devlin have them believe her to be?

99. Also More Difficult

It may have been some geological freak, but each letter here stands for a different figure. What do you make the value of that OPAL?

```
D U G ) O O L I T I C ( O P A L
        D U G
        ───────
        D T G T
        D O I A
        ───────
          I U A I
          I D U T
          ───────
            G C A C
            O U O T
            ───────
              L T I
```

100. It's the Cents That Matter

Ruth wasn't away long. She only had to run over to Spadina and back. 'That's fine,' said Hilda, looking at the buttons she'd bought, 'but I hope they only charged you at twenty-eight cents a dozen.'

Ruth took a crumpled check out of her bag. 'No, I told him we use five on each blouse and he charged at twelve cents for that number,' she told her boss.

Hilda glanced at the check. 'Well, it doesn't make that much difference,' she said, 'as on this little lot you paid only a couple of cents extra that way.'

But it's those odd cents that matter, of course. So how many buttons did Ruth buy?

101. Up in the Clouds

The professor was busy with his notes, muttering something about orthogonal functions in vector space, when the driver's voice brought him down to earth. 'Here we are, sir. Elm Crescent. But what number d'you want?'

The great mathematician has no mind for mere figures, of course. 'I'm afraid I've forgotten,' he admitted ruefully, 'but maybe you can find it for me.'

'With fifty houses in this road?' the driver started to protest. But the old gentleman interrupted him. 'No, my good man. You may be able to make sense of what my youngest boy once told me. Reverse the figures and add that to the original number and then multiply by eleven, and that gives the number of my house multiplied by itself.'

Whew! Fortunately that taxi driver had a sense of humour. He had heard of this odd character but had never before picked him up. And he *did* figure out that number.

But what do you make it?

102. Shelling Peas

Jack and Jill had been given a big basket of peas to shell. Jack started alone, and worked steadily for two-thirds of the time his sister would have taken to do the whole job herself. At that point he stopped. 'I'm through, so you can finish them,' he told her.

Jill then took his place and did the rest of the peas alone. It was dull work, but she watched the clock and did some thinking. When the last pod had been emptied she called her brother. 'If we'd worked together all the time, they'd have been finished twelve minutes sooner,' she said, 'and you'd have done exactly the same amount of shelling.'

Her figuring was right. So how long would Jack have taken to shell all those peas himself?

103. With a Hole in His Pocket

'Is that all you've got?' asked Pam, as her brother counted the quarters and nickels he'd taken out of his pocket.

'Not quite,' replied Pete, delving into the other pocket. 'I've got some dimes here where there's no hole for them to fall through.' He jingled the coins temptingly. 'So I've got three dollars ninety altogether, but it would be sixty cents less if the dimes were quarters and the quarters dimes.'

Pete had less than a couple of dozen coins altogether, but what were they?

104. One Man Stayed at Home

'Ding!' pealed the bell of St Mark's. 'Dong!' went the bell of St Jude's just a second later. 'Doong!' boomed the deep voice of St Paul's only one second after that.

And Jim still sat in his chair, making no move while the bells continued to call the stragglers to church. He had been sitting there quite a while, watch in hand, timing those bells.

The throaty bass of St Paul's sounded every twenty-three seconds; the toll of St Jude's every nineteen seconds; the silvery peal of St Mark's every seventeen seconds. Jim had satisfied himself about that. And now, having heard the three peal in rapid succession at intervals of one second, he was almost ready to go.

'But I'll wait until they all toll exactly together,' he told himself. And so he waited, and his head nodded, and he was asleep. And that's why Jim missed church that Sunday.

How long would he have had to wait for the moment of simultaneous pealing after that first chime of St Mark's with which this little story starts?

105. How It's Done

'How do you make up an alphametic?' That's quite a regular question, and so maybe an example will not be out of place.

One way is to start with a short phrase, something that *might* make sense. Say we want to make it a matter of long division, like this:

C A T) C A U G H T (H A T

Then we decide that CAT must divide exactly HAT times into CAUGHT without any remainder. So with no particular malice aforethought, we give arbitrary values to some of the letters, thus:

3 A T) 3 A 0 5 9 T (9 A T

And now comes the tricky part. We have to find values for A and T that will produce the desired result. And of course each letter has to stand for a different figure.

You may like to finish this yourself.

106. Wedding Bells

Memory plays strange tricks. Petty details from years ago come back fresh and vivid, while the more important fact of yesterday is forgotten.

It was like that with Steve. He had spent an evening with five friends discussing marriage, making notes with a view to writing an article for his editor; but he had not bothered to write in all the names. Next day he found he had quite forgotten, and had a terrible job connecting up all the dates and places with the men concerned.

His friends were Bob, John, Jack, Joe, and Bill. He himself had married in Dublin, but the others had wed in cities even further afield: Tokyo, Montreal, Cairo, Chicago, and Toronto. John had been married the longest, the six men having wed three, four, seven, twelve, sixteen, and twenty years ago. Steve had been married as long as Bob and Joe together, while Jack married even before Steve.

The Tokyo wedding was only three years ago, and the Toronto wedding preceded the ceremony in Cairo. Bill had been telling Jack about his last visit to Europe and teasing him for having never been out of Canada. Jack had been married three times as long as Bob, who had never set foot east of Suez.

These were the somewhat disconnected facts he had noted, but Steve did manage to figure out how long each of his friends had been married, and where. What do you make of it?

107. Those Squumbers

'Look, Dad!' cried Tim, pointing to the car ahead. 'That's another squumber for my list.'

His father looked completely mystified. 'What in heck's a squumber?' he asked.

Tim pulled a bit of paper from his pocket. 'It's a special sort of four-figure number on a car,' he explained. 'A kid at school started it, as their number is two nought two five— that's a squumber. You add the first half to the second half and you get forty-five, and forty-five squared brings you back to the original squumber.'

It sounded complicated, but his father saw what he meant. 'There can't be many numbers like that,' he commented.

Tim was adding his latest squumber to the list and so ignored his father's remark. But what other squumbers are there apart from that 2025?

108. At the Factory

Planning production in the holiday season when machines get their annual overhaul can be a real problem in the small factory. With several small but urgent orders in hand, Bert was trying to fit in this new rush order for ten thousand spring clips. He had only three machines free, and felt he must keep one in reserve for emergencies.

And even those three machines had very different output. The new KX 31 by itself could do the whole job in twelve hours, but even that would be too long. Two machines on the job, the KX 31 and the slower FN 20, would complete the order in eleven hours and twenty minutes less than the old BL 17 would take by itself, but that was running it too fine.

What to do? And precious minutes were passing as Bert tried to figure it out. At last he decided to use the BL 17 and the KX 31 and hope for the best. Together they should do the job in seven hours and forty-eight minutes less than the FN 20 would take, and he would still have that machine free.

So how long would the FN 20 have taken by itself?

109. Iced and Spiced

It was Ann's birthday, and her mother had baked her a lovely cake—a real cake with good things in it, not one of those cardboardy confections that come out of a packet. And the cake looked beautiful, with little candles grouped on the smooth icing.

There was a candle for each year of Ann's age, of course. And if she had been one year older than twice as old as she would have been if she had been a third as old as she would have been if she had been a year younger than half as old as she was, there would have been just a quarter as many candles on that cake as the figures of her actual age reversed.

So how old was Ann?

110. Business with Pleasure

Mike's one of those very plausible 'age-next-birthday' men—he sells life insurance. And he really does know something about figures.

When Jim met him in the club recently, Mike seemed jubilant. 'Made a cold call on a widow today, and wrote them all,' he told his friend.

'What's "all"? Wasn't one widow enough for you?' Jim asked.

'She's got two kids,' said Mike, 'and I took applications on them as well as herself.'

'So you dazzled the dame,' commented Jim. 'Or is she past that age?'

Mike chuckled appreciatively. 'If you add together the ages-next-birthday of the children, and multiply by her age-next-birthday added to the boy's, and then divide by her age-next-birthday added to the girl's, you get fourteen.' He paused a moment to let it sink in. 'And their three ages-next-birthday add up to forty-seven and the kids aren't twins.'

Jim is still wondering. But what do you make the lady's age?

111. A Deal in Kettles

Young Alf bought a small lot of cheap tea kettles with the idea of selling door-to-door. Coming home after his first day he was greeted by his wife. 'What luck?' she asked.

'Sold all I took,' he boasted, 'and for fifty dollars and nineteen cents.'

Sarah's a realist. 'Not much profit in that,' she commented. 'They cost you over a dollar fifty each.'

But Alf knew better. 'People like bargains,' he told her. 'I marked them all at five bucks and crossed that out and chalked on a lower price to still give a profit.' He smiled at the look on his wife's face. 'The dames fell for it and I got turnover.'

Sarah had to admit he was probably right, but she knew how many kettles he'd taken out that day. Do *you* know?

112. Just One of a Crowd

Sam says he's got too many brothers and sisters.

If two of his sisters were brothers, he'd have one less than twice as many brothers as he'd have sisters if two of his brothers were sisters and one of his sisters a brother.

And if one of his sisters were a brother, he'd have one less than three times as many brothers as sisters.

When you've figured it out you'll sympathize with Sam.

113. A Tale of Woe

Tom's a good salesman but he wasn't finding things too easy just then. 'Never known it so quiet,' he grumbled when Steve met him at the hotel, 'but I guess I'm getting my share of what business there is.'

He inhaled appreciatively and continued with his tale of woe—salesmen, like farmers, never admit they're doing well.

'Last week I worked hard Monday through Friday and all I earned was peanuts. Monday I made sixty cents more than my average for the five days; Friday brought me sixty cents less than I averaged on Thursday and Wednesday; Thursday I earned sixty cents more than my average for the preceding three days; and Wednesday I made sixty cents less than the average of Monday and Tuesday.'

He drew a deep breath and stubbed out his cigar.

'I see what you mean,' commented Steve. 'But what about Tuesday?'

'Exactly twelve bucks that day,' Tom told him, 'and that barely paid expenses.'

Maybe you can figure out his earnings for that week.

114. Old Masters

There must be a previous letter on its way, bogged down in the mail, for the first news I had of Bill's marriage was in a letter today; and there he mentions his wife so casually that he doesn't even give her name. He writes from Vancouver, where they seem to have met two other couples with the same interest in art.

Most of this letter is devoted to describing a sale of pictures that they all attended. It's in that that he gives the names of the three girls and of the men, but there's no hint as to which girl is Mrs Bill.

Each of the six, he says, bought as many pictures as the number of dollars he or she spent per picture, and each man spent exactly forty-eight dollars more than his wife. It seems they went a bit wild at that sale.

Bill is always one for details, and he goes on to say that he bought nine pictures more than Betty, and John seven more than Ruth. Gwen, the third girl, landed what they hope may be a Vermeer (but it's not likely at the price).

That's all Bill tells me about the girls, so I'm waiting for the missing letter. Maybe you can figure out which of them is his wife.

115. When Partners Agree

'So that's it!' concluded Clem, laying down the paper from which he had been quoting. 'A final profit of seven thousand dollars on the first year, and we'll divide it in proportion to our respective investments and months in the firm.'

His two partners looked pleased. 'That's fine,' said Doug. 'Six hundred bucks for me on my five-hundred-dollar investment.'

'Yes,' agreed Ben, 'and I get sixteen hundred on the thousand I put in.'

Clem nodded. 'I started the business with just two thousand on April 1st last year, but it was too much for me alone and I'm sure glad you both came in. It's a pity you didn't join us earlier, Doug.'

So that's the question. When did Doug join the firm?

116. Those Paper Bags

Mrs Muggins was in trouble again. She went out in the rain and bought some fruit, but on her way home the bag burst and all the oranges and grapefruit skittered over the sidewalk. She feared she hadn't recovered some of them.

'But don't you know what you bought?' asked Ted when his mother got home and told him about it.

'That's the trouble,' sighed Mrs Muggins. 'I only remember that the oranges were six cents each and that the grapefruit cost as many cents as the number of oranges I got.'

There was nothing Ted could do about it, not even when his mother told him she'd spent a dollar sixty-nine on those fruits. But maybe you can figure out how many oranges she bought.

117. Think of a Number

'Think of a number!' begged Ken.

'Not me,' replied his father. 'You think of one, and make it three figures if you can count so far.'

'Okay, Dad!' The boy waited expectantly. 'Double it,' he was told, 'and then take away one.'

Ken nodded. 'Now,' continued his father, 'shift the first figure of what you've got and make it the last figure.'

'You mean the other two figures move over to the left?' asked the boy.

'That's right,' said his father. 'And now what have you got?'

'The number I started with,' announced Ken, and that wasn't at all what his father expected. It's no use trying tricks if your memory is bad.

What *was* that number, incidentally?

118. It Pays to Pay Well

'So you've got some togs at last!' said Mary, as her husband came in wearing a smart sports jacket and new flannel pants. 'What did you pay?'

'They weren't cheap,' replied Joe, 'but it's no saving to get cheap clothes. If the coat had cost nine dollars less, a third of the total cost would have been on the pants, but if the pants had been three dollars less, three-quarters of the total would have been on the coat.'

Mary wasn't forgetting that remark about cheap clothes—she might want to remind him of it one day!—but how much had Joe paid for the outfit?

119. A Girl Awheel

Bert and Ben are twins and even their wives get mixed. Alike in their ways, they both have a horror of speeding and they both drive always at the same steady crawl. Last week they both made the long run from Brandon to Regina, driving on the same fine highway but starting at different times.

Ninety miles from Regina, Bert passed a hearse that was proceeding in the same direction at an appropriate speed of four-and-a-half miles an hour. 'Cluttering up the road,' he growled, barely remembering to raise his hat. Two hours later he met a pretty girl on a bicycle, pedalling along at a steady six-and-three-quarter miles an hour, though he didn't know that. Bert disapproves of females on bicycles anyway, so he passed without a second glance.

When eventually they met in Regina, the brothers discussed the trip. Ben had also passed the hearse, but at a point seventy-five miles from Regina. And he had passed the same girl, he told his brother, exactly forty minutes before he reached the old ruined farm. 'And that is thirty-three miles from here,' he reminded him. Ben didn't know, of course, but she hadn't stopped at all between meeting one and the other.

There's one detail missing from this very prosaic account of an exciting day, but maybe you can figure it out yourself. At what speed did they drive?

120. All the Ones

Yes, all the ones are shown in this division sum, but the other figures are indicated by x's. It isn't at all easy, but you may be able to identify the six-figure number.

```
x x x ) 1 x x 1 x 1 ( x x x
          x x x
        ---------
          1 x x x
          1 x x x
        ---------
            1 x 1 1
            1 x 1 1
          ---------
            - - - -
```

121. The Old Church Clock

'Get on with your breakfast,' exclaimed Sally, 'and stop looking out the window. You give me the jitters jumping up and down.'

Pete returned to the table with a sulky look on his face. 'It's the old church clock,' he grumbled. 'It's stopped again, and now I'll be late for work.'

His mother wasn't unduly surprised, but she went over to the window to make sure. 'I guess it stopped only a few minutes ago,' she commented, noting that the minute hand was exactly on a minute division and the hour hand just two divisions ahead.

So what time did the clock show?

122. A Generous Offer

Jack was smiling when he came into the room. 'Look, Jill!' he said. 'See what Uncle Frank just gave me.' He put some coins on the table, keeping his hand ready to save his treasure in case of need.

'That's swell!' cried Jill. 'And just when I've spent my last cent.'

'So what's that to me?' her brother teased. 'Okay, they're all dimes and quarters, three eighty-five altogether. If the dimes were quarters and the quarters dimes, there'd be less than three bucks.' He scrabbled the coins invitingly. 'You can have the dimes if you guess how many quarters there are.'

He's a nice brother. But what would you say?

123. Only the Bank Worries

Spring is always a bad time for Mike's bank manager. Mike himself never gives the state of his checking account a thought, but his four youngsters all have their birthdays within a few weeks of each other in the early part of the year, and their father is always generous.

Paddy, the youngest boy, has his birthday in April. Then there's Sheila, who celebrates hers twenty-three days earlier. Liam was born in January, his birthday being fifteen days before Sean's and Sean's is twenty-two days before Sheila's.

Mike forgot about Leap Year when he told Jim this, but one can well understand what a worry it must all be for his bank.

What do you make Sheila's birthday?

124. Her Brother's Words

'If Gwen were twice as old as one year less than the difference between her age and what mine would be if I were twice as old as one year more than the difference between my age and hers would be if she were twice as old as she would be if she were one year older than half my age, she'd be three years older than she is.'

That's what Tom told me on Gwen's birthday, but you'll have to figure out her age yourself.

125. When Nights Grow Cold

'I've flushed it through and drained it empty, Dad,' said Dick. 'What'll I do now?'

His father put down the grease-gun and came round to the front of the car. 'The man said to use a fifty-fifty mixture, and I guess it holds two gallons,' he said. 'So pour in one gallon of the anti-freeze and then add a gallon of water.' This wasn't the best way to mix them, but people seldom read the instructions.

Dick started to do as he was told, but suddenly cried out: 'It's full and I've only put in half a gallon of water.' He looked inquiringly at his father. 'So now I'll have to drain some out and then fill up again with water.'

His father nodded. 'That's right,' he told the boy. 'And I'll run the engine a while to mix it properly while you figure out how much to drain away.'

How much would you have said?

126. Island in the Sun

This isn't that old tale of sailors stranded on a tropic isle. There's a handsome sailor, certainly, but with a gorgeous blonde—sole survivors of a disaster at sea. And they had been on that lush islet several days, still finding nothing to do to pass the time waiting for possible rescue.

It was Neil's suggestion, and now they had collected a couple of hundred or so of the coconuts that abounded there. And then maybe to keep their minds off other things, he had an idea for sharing them out.

'Put aside three for the monkeys,' said Neil, 'and then take a quarter of the rest.' Beryl shrugged an inviting shoulder, but complied without demur.

Then he set aside two for the monkeys and took a quarter of what remained. What a man! Beryl thought so too. 'What now?' she asked.

Neil had it all planned. 'Set one aside this time, and then take a quarter of what's left.' When she had done so he took just a quarter of the much-diminished heap and then looked around for the monkeys you'd expect to find on a coral strand.

The girl must have guessed his thoughts. 'There's only one ape here,' she jeered, sweeping the six coconuts they had set aside back on to the main heap, 'so now we'll share all these equally.'

And that was the way they amused themselves day in and day out until they were picked up by a passing ship (that's *their* story!).

How many coconuts did they collect the first time?

127. All of a Pattern

The knives and forks looked good stacked there on the counter. 'I'll pay for them right now,' Mrs Brown told the clerk, handing him a crisp twenty-dollar bill.

The man checked the flatware. 'I'm afraid that's not quite enough, Madame.' He was very tactful. 'You chose one of our better styles, of course—not a cheap line at under fifty cents. So I'll want eighty-nine cents more, please.'

Poor Mrs Brown. She does get so confused. That bill would have been just right if she had bought half as many forks and five more of those knives. But they were really wonderful value at less than a dollar, and so she gladly paid the additional amount.

How many of each did she buy?

128. An Apple a Day

They'd been warned so many times. 'An apple a day's fine, but not too many and not too green,' their mother always said. But children have to buy experience the hard way, the same as their elders.

So Tim had to eat two-thirds as many of those unripe pippins as Tom would have eaten if Tom had eaten six more than half as many as Tim would have eaten if Tim had eaten three less than Tom would have eaten.

And how many apples does that make for Tim's tummy-ache?

129. A Good Investment

'You always tell me to save,' grumbled Kim, 'but it doesn't do any good lying in a box!'

His mother smiled. She often felt that way herself. 'I tell you what we'll do,' she told him. 'Starting today you put a penny, a dime, and a quarter into this empty piggy-bank every week. And as soon as you've saved up an exact number of dollars, I'll add five dollars to it.'

The boy wasn't going to miss the chance of that bonus, so he followed the routine faithfully. Many weeks passed, and then one day he claimed the promised prize.

How much had he saved then?

130. A Girl Can't Always Tell

Gwen's a pretty girl, and she's also remarkably intelligent, though she sometimes does go too far. Take just one of her exploits, for example.

She was applying for a job as a secretary, and when she saw the twinkle in the man's eyes, she felt sure she'd get the job despite her comparative inexperience with a typewriter.

'If you dictated two-thirds as fast as I'd type if I typed half as fast as you'd dictate if you dictated at twenty words a minute faster than I type,' she told him in answer to a question, 'you'd dictate only half as fast as I type.'

But the gleam came from contact lenses and she didn't get that job. So what do you make Gwen's typing speed?

131. A Growing Horror

Something tugged at my sleeve. Looking down I saw a strange little creature, tiny but with a huge domed head, his wizened face framing enormous staring eyes. 'Please, Mister,' he squeaked, 'we're hungry!' At that I saw he was not alone. Behind him, smaller but even more hideous, were three others of the same breed.

Biting deep into the hand with which I offered some cents, he dropped a book in his eagerness—a simple little treatise on Einstein's Theory. 'Come on,' he continued, chewing avidly. 'Didn't you hear me?'

'Why, yes,' I replied dully, offering him the other hand. 'But are they your brothers?'

He waved a slide-rule. 'Sure. And their ages total six years more than mine,' he said, spitting out a bone or two. And then, growing larger as he spoke, he informed me that the squares of the ages of the two youngest added up to thirty-six less than the sum of the squares of the ages of the other brother and himself.

'And if you multiply together the ages of the two youngest and add that to the product of the other's age and mine,' he boomed, grinding an iron-shod heel into my face as I cowered beneath him, 'you get forty-two.'

I looked up and down the vast expanse of street for help, but in vain. 'And I'll tell you something,' my tormentor concluded, a diabolical grin on his bloody face as he wrenched an arm from my poor body. 'The cube of my age equals the sum of the cubes of the ages of my three brothers.'

My shrieks must have aroused the neighbours, but that nightmare did make sense. Can you figure out the ages of the four?

132. All for 100 Kuks

In the chronicles of Kalota it is recorded that a certain farmer sold some cattle for a total of one hundred kuks—there were the 'good old days' even in that strange island.

He got fifty kees a head for calves, five kuks for each cow, and ten kuks per bull. There were one hundred kees in a kuk, the same as there are now.

The record shows that he sold just a hundred head, but gives no other details of the sale, though it obviously included at least one beast in each category.

Maybe you can figure out how many calves he must have sold.

133. A Nickel at Stake

'What's that?' asked Bill.

The small boy looked sulky. 'You never listen, Dad!' But he didn't want to lose a possible ally, so he started again. 'Bert says I owe him a nickel, and I told him I'd pay only if you said so.'

His father laughed. 'Well, what was the gag?'

'He bet me he has two cents more than a third of what I'd have if I had two cents more than a third of what he'd have if he had two cents more than a third of what I have,' explained the boy. 'And I've got exactly twelve cents.'

Bill's mind worked fast. 'Then you win,' he chuckled.

But did he?

134. Then the Tractors Came

'Prices have sure gone up,' said the old man, 'and there's all them new-fangled machines, but I doubt we farmers are any better off.'

Charles nodded. That might go for city folk too. 'Yes,' continued the farmer. 'I remember when a pig cost me two dollars more than a sheep, and a calf two dollars more than a pig.'

'Sounds cheap to me,' commented Charles.

'We didn't think so,' he was assured. The old man chewed the stem of his ancient pipe. 'That was the time I bought some calves, some sheep, and some pigs—forty-seven altogether—and there was as many more pigs than calves as the number of sheep I could have got for eighteen dollars.'

The old man paused and scratched his head. 'But dang me if I haven't forgot how much I spent on them, but I know it was the same amount on each sort of beast.'

He had forgotten. Can you figure out the total amount?

135. *Not Today, Thank You!*

'How did you make out?' asked Betty as her husband came into the livingroom. It had been the first day on his new job, and it can be tough selling door-to-door.

'Fine, dear,' Doug replied cheerfully. 'I chose a good district. Might have done even better if I hadn't been carrying only slips and nylons.' He glanced at some figures on a scrap of paper. 'Nylons sold best and I unloaded them at three-quarters of the places I tried, and two-thirds of my calls sold slips.'

'Must be your blue eyes, darling,' laughed his wife. 'Did you sell both at any of the houses?'

Doug grinned happily. 'Sure. At ten places.'

Not bad for his first day. But how many calls had he made?

136. *It's in the Paper*

'Did you read about the twins, dear?' asked Mike, manoeuvring the marmalade clear of his newspaper.

'I don't think so,' replied Mary, 'but was there something special?'

'You wait!' chuckled her husband, with a wink to Tim across the table. 'Listen to this.'

He started reading. 'Twins, born last Monday to Mrs Joe Kench, may well have set a world record for weight.' He paused to sip his coffee. 'Roy, as he will be named, weighed a third of his brother's weight, plus their combined weights multiplied by the difference between their weights divided by three pounds more than the difference between their weights.'

'Oh, stop it, Mike!' laughed Mary.

'But it's here,' she was assured, 'and that's not all.' Rather more slowly, Mike continued. 'It says their combined weights, divided by one pound less than Roy's weight, was the same as the difference between their weights.'

Tim, who had listened to all of this without a word, slipped away at that point. For the rest of Saturday morning the boy was very quiet, busy in his room. When he emerged at last and announced the weights of those twins, his mother had to find that little news item to confirm that the real version agreed with his figures.

But what do you make of it?

137. *Just Room to Shuffle*

'What say we leave now and go over to our place?' suggested Jim. 'It's too crowded here.'

His wife, with whom he had just been dancing, thought it a good idea. 'Yes, come on,' she begged the others. 'We've each had a dance with each of the men and that's plenty!'

Ruth flashed her a quick smile and then turned to her own husband. 'My feet still ache from what you did to them during the first dance,' she told him, 'so I'm ready to go.'

Bob is always easy. He'd had the second dance with Gwen and the third with his wife, but he's no dancer. 'Count me in on whatever you all decide,' was his comment.

Steve nodded. 'And that goes for me too,' he said.

But Jim wasn't sure about the other two girls. He turned to Ann, who had just had the last dance with Tom. 'What about you?' he asked.

Ann seemed to be thinking, but Mary answered Jim's question. 'She's worrying about the sitter,' she laughed, pushing back her chair, 'and it's quite a while since that second dance I had with you, but let's go.'

And so, having stayed there for only four dances, the four men drove their wives over to Jim's home.

Do you know the names of Tom's wife and Gwen's husband?

89

138. Really Difficult

It's no use pretending this is easy. Each figure is represented by either a code letter or an x, and it must be understood that a figure might appear in code in one place but as an x in another. Each code letter stands for a different figure, of course. So now you are asked to decode NEAR:

```
N E A R ) X X X X X R ( A R E
        N E A R
        X X X X X
        X X X X N
          X X X X X
          X X X X N
              N R N
```

139. The Baby of the Family

If John were three years older than three times as old as Jane would be if she were half his age older than she would be if she were two years older than half as old as he was when he was a year older than three times as old as Jane was, he would be five times Jane's age older than he is.

We have taken both their ages in round figures, of course —not bothering about odd months. Jane is only a child, but how old is John?

140. *Small Boys Like Apples*

'Just keep your paws off while I count them,' said Bob, checking the apples his mother had brought into the recreation room for the boys. He had some of his friends in, and Mrs Morgan had put a large basket of luscious pippins on the table for them.

'Okay, we'll start.' Bob can be very methodical. 'You take your share, Harry.'

'But what's that?' asked Harold.

'Don't you know what "share" means, stupid?' his young host replied politely. 'If there were four of us you'd take a quarter, or a third if we were three.'

Harold went rather red but took his proper share as ordered.

'Now it's your turn, Jack,' Bob continued.

Jack counted the remaining apples, divided them into equal lots and took one lot. This didn't meet with Bob's approval, however. 'You made one lot too many,' he declared, 'so you're short on your share.'

'Yes, I guess I forgot Harry's had his,' rejoined Jack, turning away from the table, 'but that's plenty for me and we've got them in our own orchard.'

That left Bob with a problem, but he handled the rest of the distribution himself and the boys were soon munching happily. And despite his words, it didn't take Jack long to finish the seven apples he had taken.

How many boys were there?

141. For the Long Room

'I've got a surprise for you, dear,' said Steve coming into the livingroom. 'A new carpet, and it cost all of a hundred and eighty-eight bucks.'

'But how wonderful!' Mary threw her arms around his neck. 'What's it like, and how big?'

'Just a rug,' replied her husband. 'Reds and greens, but it seemed right for the drapes.'

'And the size?' persisted Mary. 'This room's such a long shape.'

'It'll nearly cover the floor,' Steve assured her. 'I could have got the same thing two feet longer but one foot narrower at exactly the same price, for the area would have been the same. It's too bad the room isn't more square as there was one very attractive rug, three feet wider than ours but four feet shorter, covering the same area but fifty dollars cheaper.'

The one he bought was a bargain, anyway. But what did it cost per square yard?

142. No Heart on His Sleeve

'I'll never forget that leave I first met you,' said Jack, looking up from some old snapshots.

Sally smiled. She could never forget either. She still recalled the thrill of meeting the tall soldier, so handsome in his uniform, and she now waited for her husband's next words.

'It was such dreadful weather,' he went on, not realizing how words could hurt. 'When it rained in the afternoon it was fine in the morning, but it did rain seven days of that leave and there were only five fine afternoons and six fine mornings.'

Sally shook away her disappointment—he had never been one for sentiment. But how long was that wartime leave he remembered so well?

143. A Bad Start

It was one of those hot, humid days when people should not have to work. It was also Bill's first day in the new job, and he was in trouble already over an invoice. 'I can't make out what in the heck you did,' growled his boss, 'but anyway you charged fifty-nine dollars too little for these.' He pointed to the form.

'Gee, Mr Gill,' stammered the boy, 'that's awful.' Nervous and confused, he checked the total. It seemed so simple: just one lot of knives at a dollar each less 33⅓ % discount— not even a thousand of them. Bill couldn't figure out how he'd got it wrong, but wrong it was and by the amount Mr Gill had said. 'I'll do it again,' he mumbled, reaching for fresh forms from the rack.

His boss chuckled. 'We're go-ahead folk here,' he told Bill, 'so no more going backwards. Instead of allowing the discount, you merely reversed the gross amount in dollars.' And that's just what he had done.

How many knives had to be charged in that lot?

144. It Could Happen Here

'You want my age?' the lady cried,
Surprised and rather horrified.
'If that's the price I have to pay
To get a drink, why, then I'll say:
When multiplied by just five more,
My age makes tum tum seven four.'
She smiled and shook her curly head.
'My grandson's nearly twelve years wed!'
The barman laughed. She got her drink.
But was she old enough, d'you think?

145. Cakes for the Kids

Uncle Frank had given his three nephews sixty cents each to spend at the Vienna Bakery around the corner, and now they were back. 'I hope you found what you wanted,' he said as the boys trooped into the garden.

'Sure,' replied Ron, offering a luscious cream confection. 'We each chose our favourite. Take one, they're good.'

'Try one of mine first,' Roy chipped in. 'They're better and they cost three cents each more than his.'

'We won't fight about it,' laughed their uncle. 'I'm afraid I never eat cakes, but maybe your mother can judge when we have tea.'

Reg, the eldest boy, had been standing aloof—he's the serious one of the family. 'Mine are a bit cheaper,' he now remarked, 'but Mum loves them too. They cost as many cents each as the number of his cakes Ron could have bought for eight times what Roy paid for each of his.'

That took some figuring out, but Uncle Frank managed it before his sister called them all into the house for tea. So how many cakes did Reg buy?

146. *One Girl Away*

Joe's little factory had been almost closed down for some weeks, but now production had started again. 'We've turned out a hundred and two dresses these first two days,' he told Charles when they met on Tuesday evening, 'and everything's fine.'

'Sounds a lot for a small shop,' commented his friend, who knows nothing about the trade.

'It is,' replied Joe, 'but I've got good operators. Yesterday they each made the same number and made them well.'

Charles nodded. 'I'm sure of that,' he rejoined, knowing the other's views on efficiency.

'And today one of the girls was sick,' continued Joe, 'but the others worked only a fraction faster and they each made three more dresses than yesterday.'

That shows the good feeling in Joe's place. But then it is a tiny concern, as you will realize when you figure out how many girls he had working on that Monday.

147. The Bird Watchers

Would you think it fun to stand for hours in the bush just to check on birds that might come your way? That's what twenty-seven enthusiasts are reported to have done for a recent census of the feathered fraternity. And among them they counted birds of more than thirty different species—one watcher even reported a rare mourning-dove near Port Arthur.

But those men were tough, and the ten women watchers too. Only nine of the party were able to reach their posts by car, the rest having to depend on their own sturdy legs to reach points inaccessible awheel.

For most of them it must have been an interesting and satisfying experience, as only five watchers noted less than a dozen different species each.

Maybe you can figure out the minimum number of male watchers who, having reached their posts on foot, must have reported twelve or more species of birds that day.

148. Crime After Midnight

So easy! The old watchman lay quiet—secured, bound, and gagged—and now they could crack the safe at their leisure.

It took only a few minutes to place a rag-shot; only minutes to drill the small hole just above the lock, to push in a strip of cloth well soaked in nitro, to follow that with a tiny detonator, to plug the vent with soap.

A gentle *whoosh* and the door swung open. And there lay the loot, all in much-used, untraceable five-dollar bills. 'No tens,' growled Dice the triggerman. 'No other cash at all.'

'So what's the difference? There's the best part of a thousand bucks there,' retorted the light-fingered Lanski.

The three petermen were taking no more chances. Every move had been planned. They'd share the loot right there and then get out of town quickly and separately.

McHusky, the brains behind the job, now took charge. 'Here's five bucks for him,' he chuckled, flipping a bill from the pile over towards the trussed figure on the floor, 'and now I take my third of what's left.' That being done, he proceeded. He took another bill from the pile and dropped it on their victim. 'Now you take a third of what's left,' he told Lanski.

The watchman received a third bill from the pile, and then Dice took a third of what remained. Then on a sudden whim of their leader they divided the rest among them in the ratio of 2 to 3 to 4—McHusky taking the smallest share in that final division and Dice the largest.

And so they shared the loot exactly, with no argument over any odd bills left over. Now we only want to know how much those three crooks found in the safe.

149. In Father's Footsteps

'He's a fine young man,' said Bill, as his friend's son left the room, 'but I've known you three years, so how come we never met before?'

Bert smiled. 'He's been over in Europe most of the time, studying,' he replied, 'but now we hope he'll stick around for a while.'

'What about going in with you?' asked Bill. 'I guess you'd like that.'

'Of course!' Bert nodded. 'In fact I've just offered him a partnership when he's thirty.'

'Always the canny Scot—let him prove himself first!' Bill laughed. 'But how old is he now?'

For a moment there was silence, and then his friend replied in true Bertian style: 'When I'm double his present age, not counting the odd months,' he said, 'he'll be just two-thirds as old as the reverse of what my age will be then.'

And it was only after he returned home that Bill figured out the answer to his question. What do you make it?

150. *Until We Meet Again*

'Goodbye!' 'Goodbye!' The party had broken up and Molly's guests were leaving.

Very soon the last of them had departed and Molly, having bolted the door of her apartment, sank into a chair for a few moments of relaxation before clearing the glasses and ashtrays.

'Life's so full of "goodbyes",' she mused. 'A meaningless little word—the saddest word of all.' And then she recalled something she had noticed when her guests bade her and each other farewell.

The word 'goodbye' had been used only once by any one person to any other person: each guest had said 'goodbye' to her and she had said 'goodbye' to each guest. Each single guest had said 'goodbye' to each of the other guests. The married guests had each said 'goodbye' to each of the other guests but not, of course, to their own spouses. All the married guests had come to the party with their own husbands or wives and had left with them.

That's as far as Molly went before she fell asleep in her chair. But as the word 'goodbye' had been spoken fifty-two times altogether, you'll be able to figure out how many married couples she had entertained.

TYPICAL SOLUTIONS

TYPICAL SOLUTION A

1. Walt's Waxworks

First day: x men @ a¢, y women @ b¢, z children @ c¢.

From Walt's 'ifs and ands' we get the equations:

$$a (x + y + z) = 3000 \qquad b (x + y + z) = 1500$$
$$c (x + y + z) = 600$$

Dividing the first and second by the third equation, we get

$$a = 5c \quad \text{and } b = \frac{5c}{2}$$

From Walt's final statement, $a + b + c = 85$

So $5c + \dfrac{5c}{2} + c = 85$, whence $17c + 170$, hence $c = 10$.

Thus we have $a = 50$, $b = 25$, $c = 10$.

So, as $10(x + y + z) = 600$, we have $x + y + z = 60$.

Using that, and also Walt's statements about the actual takings for the two days, we get:

$$\begin{aligned} x + \quad y + \quad z &= \quad 60 \\ 50x + 25y + 10z &= 2010 \\ 10x + 50y + 25z &= 1890 \end{aligned}$$

whence

$$\begin{aligned} 10x + 10y + 10z &= \quad 600 \\ 50x + 25y + 10z &= 2010 \\ 4x + 20y + 10z &= \quad 756 \end{aligned}$$

Subtracting the first and the third from the second, we get,

$$\begin{aligned} 40x + 15y &= 1410 \\ 46x + \quad 5y &= 1254 \end{aligned}$$

whence

$$\begin{aligned} 40x + 15y &= 1410 \\ 138x + 15y &= 3762 \end{aligned}$$

Subtracting one from the other, we get:

$$98x = 2352, \text{ so } x = 24.$$

Then $15y = 1410 - 960 = 450$, so $y = 30$, hence $z = 6$.

So 24 men attended the first day.

TYPICAL SOLUTION B

2. Two Friends on the Road

Let the distance between the two villages be x miles.
When they met,

John had driven 36 miles in ⅔ hours,
Bill had driven $(x - 36)$ miles in 1½ hours.

Hence their speeds were:

John: 54 m.p.h.; Bill: ⅔$(x - 36)$ m.p.h.

After they met, John drove $(x - 36)$ miles; Bill 36 miles.
But they drove these distances in the same times. Hence Bill's speed

was $\dfrac{36}{x - 36} \times 54$ m.p.h.

Each maintained a steady speed, so Bill's speed after they met was the same as his speed before they met.

So $\qquad$ ⅔$(x - 36) = \dfrac{36 \times 54}{x - 36}$ whence $x = 90$.

So the distance between the two villages was 90 miles.

TYPICAL SOLUTION C

3. Easy? Well, Maybe

There can be no set way of tackling this type of problem. In each case one must look for obvious clues based on the simple and obvious connections between ordinary numbers. This is a fairly easy example, but it does reveal some of the main principles involved in most alphametics.

A N) E E L (O H | AN $\times$ OH = EEL — AO, so
    L A | (N $\times$ H) has the same ending as
    M H L | (L — O).
    M N N | But from MHL — MNN, (L — O)
    A O | ends with N, hence (N $\times$ H) ends with N.

Clearly (AN $\times$ H) > (AN $\times$ O), so H > O.
Now O $\neq$ zero, and O $\neq$ 1, so O > 1, whence H > 2.

Then to make ($N \times H$) end with N, when $N \neq$ zero,
   H would have to be 3 or 6 or 6 or 6 or 7 or 9
with N correspondingly   5   2   4   8   5   5
But LA cannot end with zero, so N cannot be 5,
and from $MHL - MNN$, we see that $H > N$.
So we are left with $H = 6$, and $N = 2$ or 4.
From ($MHL - MNN$), $H = N + A$, or $H = N + A + 1$ (if with
'carry 1' from '$L - N$')
So we have $A =$ 4   or   2   or   3   or   1
      with $N =$ 2   4   2   4
   making $AN =$ 42   24   32   14
   whence $MNN =$ 252   144   192   84
The only acceptable case is when $MNN = 144$, hence $M = 1$.
We have proved that $H > O$, and we have $M = 1$, $A = 2$, $N = 4$,
$H = 6$, and also $O \neq$ zero, so $O = 3$ or 5.
But ($N \times O$) ends with A, i.e. with 2, so $O = 3$.
Hence, $EEL = (AN \times OH) + AO = (24 \times 36) + 23 = 887$.

TYPICAL SOLUTION D

4. Whose Glass Is It?

Mary picked x glasses @ 29¢, y tumblers @ 19¢, and the markers
cost z¢ each, where $z < 19$.
Then we get $29x + 19y = 29(x + 3) + 6z + 1$
whence $19y - 6z = 88$
This is the simplest form of 'indeterminate equation', i.e. one equation
with two unknowns. Solution depends on the fact that each unknown is a whole number.
Divide through by 6 (i.e. one of the coefficients), getting

$$3y + \frac{y}{6} - z = 15 - \frac{2}{6}$$

Now x and y are whole numbers, and z is a whole number, so
$\frac{y + 2}{6}$ must be a whole number.

Say $\dfrac{y + 2}{6} = k,$ where k is any whole number, positive, negative, or zero.

Then
$$y = 6k - 2.$$
Substitute this value for y in the original equation, getting
$$z = 19k - 21.$$
Hence the general solution of the equation is given by $y = 6k - 2,$ $z = 19k - 21,$ where any desired whole number value may be assigned to $k.$

In this particular case, z must be positive and $z < 19,$ so $k = 2.$ Hence $y = 10,$ $z = 17,$ so the markers cost 17¢ each.

TYPICAL SOLUTION E

21. Only One There

She bought x handkerchiefs @ 39¢, y @ 29¢.

Then
$$39x + 29y = 330$$
This is an indeterminate equation, but not of the most simple type (see *Typical Solution D*).

Divide through by 29:

$$x + \dfrac{10x}{29} + y = 11 + \dfrac{11}{29}, \text{ whence } \dfrac{10x - 11}{29} \text{ is a whole}$$
number.

Now multiply by 3. This multiplier is chosen as being the lowest whole-number multiplier that will make the new coefficient of x one less or one more than a multiple of 29.

So now we get $\dfrac{30x - 33}{29},$ which must be a whole number.

This becomes $x + \dfrac{x}{29} - 1 - \dfrac{4}{29}$

whence $\dfrac{x - 4}{29}$ is a whole number, say $k.$

Then $x = 29k + 4,$ and substituting this value in equation $y = 6 - 39k.$

104

In this practical case, both x and y must be positive, so $k = 0$, whence $x = 4$, $y = 6$.
So she bought 4 @ 39¢, 6 @ 29¢.

TYPICAL SOLUTION F
6. The Wheels of Commerce

Sales: third week, x cars; second week, y; first week, $(56 - x - y)$.
From data, $x^2 - (55 - y)x - 2y^2 + 57y - 56 = 0$.
This is an 'indeterminate equation of the second degree', i.e. two unknowns, including the square of one or both. Solution depends on the fact that both unknowns are whole numbers. We treat it as an ordinary quadratic, in this case in x:

$$x = \frac{(55 - y) \pm \sqrt{(9y^2 - 338y + 3249)}}{2}$$

As x and y are whole numbers, the expression under the square-root sign must be square and positive.
So let $9y^2 - 338y + 3249 = k^2$
where k is any whole number that will satisfy the square condition. Treating this as an ordinary quadratic, we get

$$y = \frac{169 \pm \sqrt{(9k^2 - 680)}}{9}$$

Again, the expression under the square-root sign must be a square, and we have to find values of k that will make it so. Trial of successive values would be laborious, but there are shorter methods:
Let $9k^2 - 680 = t^2$, where t is any whole number that will satisfy the square condition.
Then $9k^2 - t^2 = 680$, i.e. $(3k + t)(3k - t) = 680$.
Taking the factors of 680, we have:
$680 = 340 \times 2$, or 170×4, or 68×10, or 34×20.
Now tabulate these alternatives, coupled with $(3k + t)$ and $(3k - t)$, where $(3k + t)$ must be greater than $(3k - t)$.

$$3k + t = 340 \text{ or } 170 \text{ or } 68 \text{ or } 34$$
$$3k - t = \quad 2 \qquad 4 \qquad 10 \qquad 20$$

so
$$6k \quad = \overline{342} \quad \overline{174} \quad \overline{78} \quad \overline{54}$$
$$2t = 338 \qquad 166 \qquad 58 \qquad 14$$
$$k \quad = \quad 57 \qquad 29 \qquad 13 \qquad 9$$
$$t = 169 \qquad 83 \qquad 29 \qquad 7$$

making y $= \quad 0 \qquad 28 \qquad 22 \qquad 18$

whence x $= \qquad\qquad 28 \quad 23 \text{ or } 40 \quad 23 \text{ or } 14$

But, $x > y$, and $x \neq y$, so $x = 23$.

Hence they sold 23 cars the third week, sales being:

First week: 15 or 11
Second week: 18 or 22
Third week: 23   23

TYPICAL SOLUTION G
7. Bill, Bert, and Betty

The ages are: Bill, x; Bert, y; Betty $(x + y)$ years.

Working back from the statement of fact (i.e. 'he *would* be twelve years older . . .'), we get:

If Bill were 7 years older he would be $(x + 7)$.

If Bert were 11 years younger than that, he'd be $(x - 4)$.

If Bill were twice that age, he would be $2(x - 4)$.

If Bert were Betty's age added to that, he'd be $(3x + y - 8)$.

If Bill were as old as that, he'd be $(3x + y - 8)$.

Then, working back from the end of the paragraph, we do not know which is the older of the boys, so we must allow for the two possibilities:

If Bill were 12 years older than the difference between his and Bert's age, he would be $12 \pm (x - y)$. So

$$3x + y - 8 = 12 + x - y,$$
$$\text{OR } 3x + y - 8 = 12 - x + y,$$
$$\text{hence } x + y = 2 \text{ OR } x = 5$$

There is more than 10 years difference between their ages, so Bill's and Bert's ages cannot total only 2 years.

Hence $x = 5$, and Bill is 5 years old.

106

TYPICAL SOLUTION H

9. The Long Road Home

The last distance had digits x, y in that order, so it had the actual 'value' $(10x + y)$ miles.

The second distance had digits x, 0, y OR y, 0, x with actual values $(100x + y)$ OR $(x + 100y)$ miles respectively.

The first distance had digits y, z, x in that order, with actual value $(x + 100y + 10z)$ miles.

Here we shall have to examine two alternative cases, each giving an indeterminate equation of the first degree (see *Typical Solution E*) but with three unknowns. Solution will be handled on much the same lines as with two unknowns, and will depend on the fact that each is a whole-number and each is less than 10.

Say distances were x, y; x, 0, y; y, z, x.

Then $2\left\{(100x+y)-(10x+y)\right\} = (x+100y+10z)-(100x+y)$

whence $279x - 99y = 10z$

Dividing through by 10, we get the general solution:

$$x = 10k + y$$
$$z = 279k + 18y$$

but $y < 10$, so no possible whole number value for k would give a value of z to comply with $z < 10$ and z being positive.

Hence this alternative case is not acceptable.

Say the distance were x, y; y, 0, x; y, z, x.

Then $2\left\{(x+100y)-(10x+y)\right\} = (x+100y+10z)-(x+100y)$

whence $99y - 9x = 5z$

Here we see that z must be a multiple of 9, so $z = 9$.

Then $99y - 9x = 45$, whence $y = 1$, $x = 6$.

So the distances were 61, 106, and 196 miles on the sign-posts.

Hence his speed was 45 miles per hour.

TYPICAL SOLUTION I

12. So Unobservant

By the hour hand the time was x hours, y minutes.

So the minute hand showed $(y + 7)$ minutes at that time.

The hour hand moves 5 minute divisions in one hour, so when it showed x hours, y minutes, it was at the $\left(5x + \dfrac{y}{12}\right)$ minute division.

But the minute hand, at $(y + 7)$, was at the same position.

So
$$5x + \frac{y}{12} = y + 7$$

whence
$$60x - 11y = 84$$

This is an indeterminate equation (see *Typical Solution E*), which can be solved as such if we know that the two unknowns are whole numbers. In this particular problem, however, we know that $x = 8$.

Hence
$$11y = 396$$

whence
$$y = 36$$

So the hour hand showed 8.36 a.m.

TYPICAL SOLUTION J

19. On Parade

Let N be the required number of soldiers.
$$N = 5a - 1 = 6b - 1 = 7c - 1 = 11d + 1$$
where a, b, c, and d are whole numbers.

Then $(N + 1) = 5a = 6b = 7c = 11d + 2$.

Clearly $(N + 1)$ is a multiple of 5, 6, and 7.

The Lowest Common Multiple of 5, 6, and 7 is 210, so $(N + 1)$ is a multiple of 210, e.g. say $210k$ where k is a whole number.

Then
$$210k - 11d = 2$$

This is an indeterminate equation (see *Typical Solution D*).

Divide through by 11:

108

$19k + \dfrac{k}{11} - d = \dfrac{2}{11}$, so $\dfrac{k-2}{11}$ is a whole number, say t.

Then $\qquad\qquad k = 11t + 2$

whence $\qquad\qquad N = 210(11t + 2) - 1$

so $\qquad\qquad N = 2310t + 419.$

But in this case N is less than 500, so $t = 0$.

Hence N $= 419$, so he had 419 soldiers.

TYPICAL SOLUTION K

10. I've Got a Winner

List the three statements in a slightly different form but without changing their meanings:

A. Fay's Folly will be first.

B. Fay's Folly will be first or third.

C. Satan will be first or second.

If A was correct:

B would have been correct, which is impossible. So A was not correct.

If B was correct:

A must have been wrong, so Fay's Folly was not first, hence Fay's Folly would have been third.

In that case C would also have been correct, which is impossible.

So B was not correct.

Hence C was correct and we have:

B was wrong, so Fay's Folly was second.

C being right, Satan must have been first.

So Kimono was third.

ANSWERS

1. 24 men.
2. 90 miles.
3. AN EEL is 24 887.
4. 17¢ each.
5. Sally weighs 119 lbs.
6. 23 cars the third week.
7. Bill is 5 years old.
8. 11 women (3 married women without husbands, 4 with husbands, 4 spinsters).
9. 45 m.p.h.
10. Satan, Fay's Folly, Kimono.
11. 73 years old.
12. 8.36 a.m.
13. 7 nickels.
14. Total number was $3n^2 - 3n + 1$, where n is the number of counters in any outer side of the 'star'.

    $\qquad 3n^2 - 3n + 1$ is between 400 and 500

    so $\qquad 36n^2 - 36n + 12$ is between 4800 and 6000

    so $\qquad (6n - 3)^2$ is between 4797 and 5997

    Between these limits the square numbers are 4900, 5041, 5184, 5329, 5476, 5625, 5776, 5729. Of these, only 5625 will give a whole number value for n, with $n = 13$.

    So $3n^2 - 3n + 1 = 469$, and there were 469 counters.
15. $5.13.
16. The number was 5776.
17. 40 stamps.
18. 36 years old.
19. 419 soldiers.

20. $1.56 among 6.
21. 10 handkerchiefs.
22. $\sqrt{784}$ — 9
23. 71 girls 'up'.
24. THAT is 7657.
25. Tim, 17; Tom, 11.
26. 24 m.p.h.
27. The flannel suit cost $43.00 (gabardine, $50; tweed, $57).
28. The cheque was for $32.66.
29. Nineteen minutes after the hour.
30. One year old.
31. The watches cost $1.80 each.
32. 10 hours, 48 minutes altogether.
33. The number was 64.
34. 4¢ difference.
35. NEST is 9328.
36. Year 1764.
37. 72¢ for 12 oranges.
38. His age was 23 years.
39. 40 people altogether.
40. 36¢ (1 penny, 7 nickels).
41. The sides were x feet, y feet, $\sqrt{(x^2 + y^2)}$ feet: the area ½xy square feet.

We get $xy - 40x - 40y + 800 = 0$
whence $(x - 40)(y - 40) = 800$
Tabulate with factors of 800:

$x - 40 =$	20	25	32	40	50	etc.
$y - 40 =$	40	32	25	20	16	etc.
$x =$	60	65	72	80	90	etc.
$y =$	80	72	65	60	56	etc.
$\sqrt{(x^2 + y^2)} =$	100	97	97	100	106	etc.
Perimeter =	240	234	234	240	252	etc.

The perimeter must be less than 240 feet, so it is 234 feet.
So the dimensions were 65 feet by 72 feet by 97 feet.

42. Peggy had one brother.
43. 15 steps up.
44. 38 eggs altogether.
45. 40 miles.
46. BONE is 3698.
47. $72 ($64 in July).
48. Jack 21¢, Jill 92¢.
49. 73 years old.
50.

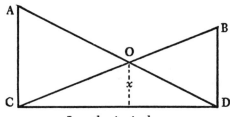

Lengths in inches:

$$BD = \sqrt{(91^2 - 84^2)} = 35 \text{ inches.}$$
$$AC = \sqrt{(105^2 - 84^2)} = 63 \text{ inches.}$$

$$\frac{CO}{CB} = \frac{x}{BD}, \text{ so } CO = \frac{91x}{35} = \frac{13x}{5}$$

$$\frac{OB}{OC} = \frac{BD}{AC}, \text{ so } OB = \frac{91x}{63} = \frac{13x}{9}$$

Now $OB + OC = 91$, so $13x (1/5 + 1/9) = 91$ whence $x = 22\frac{1}{2}$, so the height was $22\frac{1}{2}$ inches.

51. Ken was 13 years old.
52. 59 times.
53. 52 years old.
54. Exactly one hour.
55. $123 - 4 + 56 - 78 - 9.$
56. I am 109.
57. Tim, 22¢; Tam, 26¢; Tom, 34¢.
58. 3 years younger than John, so he would be 10 years old.

59. The ages were x years and y years, with $x < y$.
$x^3 + y^3 = (x + y)(x^2 - xy + y^2) = 2540$
$x < y$, so $x^3 < 1270$, hence $x < 11$,
and $y^3 < 2540$, so $y < 14$, hence $(x + y) < 24$.
Then, as $2540 = 2 \times 2 \times 5 \times 127$, we get:

$x + y =$	2	or	4	or	10	or	20
with $x^2 + 2xy + y^2 =$	4		16		100		400
and $x^2 - xy + y^2 =$	1270		635		254		127
whence $3xy =$	—ve		—ve		—ve		273

As xy must be positive, we have $xy = 91$, and $x + y = 20$.
$x < y$, so $x = 7$, $y = 13$
Hence the ages of the triplets were 7 and 13 years.
60. The time was 4.29 p.m.
61. 28 m.p.h.
62. $81.35.
63. 30 mangoes.
64. 315 articles @ 41¢.
65. 7¢, 11¢, and 13¢.
66. 12 minutes' gain.
67. 12 years old.
68. The car was 17 years old, the engine 3½ years.
69. 133 books altogether.
70. SCORE is 94587.
71. 7 pearls.
72. 8.49 o'clock.
73. She would have 5.
74. There remained $(3x + y)$ days, where $y = 0, 1,$ or 2.
Each 3 days he will smoke 29, and 13 a day for each of the
final y days (if any).
So $29x + 13y = 10(3x + y)$, whence $x = 3y$.
But it was before March the 16th, so $x > 4$, hence $y = 2$.
So $x = 6$, and the conversation was on March the 12th.
75. Jack, the artist, had tea.
76. 9 cats, 12 canaries.

77. 77 buttons.
78. 'What' is 14.
79. 6 men, 144 fish.
80. 73 years old.
81. Sam is 4, Susan is 2.
82. He lost $791, last race.
83. Number 89.
84. 3 pints each.
85. June the 11th.
86. 3670 + 3037 = 6707.
87. 6 feet long.
88. $1.55.
89. The census total was 410256.
90. 8.01 a.m.
91. 12 coins altogether.
92. 88 for the steamer.
93. 11 years old.
94. 14 lbs. of bananas.
95. $39.72 altogether.
96. $3.48 for the hat.
97.

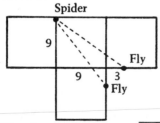

The shortest route was $\sqrt{(9^2 + 12^2)}$ = 15 feet.
98. 41 years old.
99. OPAL is 1983.
100. 30 buttons.
101. Number 22.
102. Jack would have taken 36 minutes by himself.
103. 12 quarters, 8 dimes, 2 nickels.
104. 56 minutes 23 seconds.

105. AT must be 86.
106. Joe: 3 years, Tokyo; Bob: 4 years, Chicago; Jack: 12 years, Montreal; Bill: 16 years, Cairo; John: 20 years, Toronto.
107. 3025, 9801 (and improbably 0000 and 0001).
108. 15 hours.
109. 23 years old.
110. 34 years old next birthday; the children are 5 and 8.
111. They sold at more than 150¢ but less than 500¢ each. $50.19 is 5019¢, and 5019 has factors $3 \times 7 \times 239$. Between 150 and 500, the only factor of 5019 is 239, so he sold 21 tea kettles at $2.39 each.
112. 7 brothers, 4 sisters.
113. $61.20 for the week.
114. Gwen is his wife.
115. October the 1st.
116. x oranges @ 6¢, y grapefruit @ y¢, so $x (y + 6) = 169$. Both x and y are whole numbers, and factors of 169 are 13×13. So $x = 13$, and $y + 6 = 13$. Hence $y = 7$, and he bought 13 oranges.
117. 316.
118. $45 for the coat, $18 for the pants.
119. 27 m.p.h.
120. $106191 \div 437$.
121. 7.36 a.m.
122. 13 quarters, 6 dimes.
123. Liam's birthday, in January, is 60 days before Paddy's birthday in April. So Paddy's birthday must be April the 1st, whence Sheila's is March the 9th.
124. 17 years old.
125. 3 pints.
126. 235 coconuts.
127. She bought x knives @ a¢, $2y$ forks @ b¢. Se we get $ax + 2by = 2089$, and $2ax + 2by = 4000 - 10a$ whence $a(x + 10) = 1911 = 3 \times 7 \times 7 \times 13$. a is between 50 and 99, so $a = 91$, and $x + 10 = 21$.

So $x = 11$, and $ax = 1001$, whence $by = 544$. But 544 has factors $2^5 \times 17$, and b is between 50 and 99. So $b = 68$, whence $y = 8$. So she bought 11 knives @ 91¢, 16 forks @ 68¢.

128. Tim ate 6 apples.

129. $9.

130. 40 words a minute.

131. 3, 4, 5, and 6 years.

132. 90 calves, 9 cows, 1 bull.

133. Bert would have had $3\frac{1}{3}$¢, which is impossible. So Bert lost his bet.

134. 12 calves @ $10, 15 pigs @ $8, 20 sheep @ $6.

135. 24 calls.

136. 9 lbs. and 11 lbs.

137. Mary was Tom's wife; Jim was Gwen's husband.

138. NEAR is 4318.

139. John is 26 years old.

140. 8 boys, 64 apples.

141. $11.75 per square yard.

142. 9 days.

143. 714 knives.

144. 78 years old.

145. Reg, 6; Ron, 5; Roy, 4.

146. The first day, x girls made y dresses each. Then we get $2xy + 3x - y = 105$, so $(2x - 1)(2y + 3) = 207$. From the context $(2x - 1) > 3$, and $(2y + 3) > 3$, hence $\qquad 2x - 1 = \quad$ 9 or 23
and $\qquad 2y + 3 = 23$ or $\quad$ 9
whence $x = 5$, $y = 10$, or $x = 12$, $y = 3$. But they worked 'only a fraction faster' to make 3 more dresses each, so $y = 3$. Hence $x = 5$, and there were 5 girls.

147. The minimum number of male watchers who saw twelve or more species was $(27 - 5) - 10$, i.e. 12. The minimum number of these male watchers who went on foot was $12 - 9$, i.e. 3.

148. $935.

149. 27 years old.

150. 2 couples.

CATALOGUE OF DOVER BOOKS

Books Explaining Science and Mathematics

* The more difficult books are indicated by an asterisk

WHAT IS SCIENCE?, N. Campbell. The role of experiment and measurement, the function of mathematics, the nature of scientific laws, the difference between laws and theories, the limitations of science, and many similarly provocative topics are treated clearly and without technicalities by an eminent scientist. "Still an excellent introduction to scientific philosophy," H. Margenau in PHYSICS TODAY. "A first-rate primer . . . deserves a wide audience," SCIENTIFIC AMERICAN. 192pp. 5⅜ x 8.   S43 Paperbound **$1.25**

THE NATURE OF PHYSICAL THEORY, P. W. Bridgman. A Nobel Laureate's clear, non-technical lectures on difficulties and paradoxes connected with frontier research on the physical sciences. Concerned with such central concepts as thought, logic, mathematics, relativity, probability, wave mechanics, etc. he analyzes the contributions of such men as Newton, Einstein, Bohr, Heisenberg, and many others. "Lucid and entertaining . . . recommended to anyone who wants to get some insight into current philosophies of science," THE NEW PHILOSOPHY. Index. xi + 138pp. 5⅜ x 8.   S33 Paperbound **$1.25**

EXPERIMENT AND THEORY IN PHYSICS, Max Born. A Nobel Laureate examines the nature of experiment and theory in theoretical physics and analyzes the advances made by the great physicists of our day: Heisenberg, Einstein, Bohr, Planck, Dirac, and others. The actual process of creation is detailed step-by-step by one who participated. A fine examination of the scientific method at work. 44pp. 5⅜ x 8.   S308 Paperbound **$1.00**

THE PSYCHOLOGY OF INVENTION IN THE MATHEMATICAL FIELD, J. Hadamard. The reports of such men as Descartes, Pascal, Einstein, Poincaré, and others are considered in this investigation of the method of idea-creation in mathematics and other sciences and the thinking process in general. How do ideas originate? What is the role of the unconscious? What is Poincaré's forgetting hypothesis? are some of the fascinating questions treated. A penetrating analysis of Einstein's thought processes concludes the book. xiii + 145pp. 5⅜ x 8.   T107 Paperbound **$1.25**

THE NATURE OF LIGHT AND COLOUR IN THE OPEN AIR, M. Minnaert. Why are shadows sometimes blue, sometimes green, or other colors depending on the light and surroundings? What causes mirages? Why do multiple suns and moons appear in the sky? Professor Minnaert explains these unusual phenomena and hundreds of others in simple, easy-to-understand terms based on optical laws and the properties of light and color. No mathematics is required but artists, scientists, students, and everyone fascinated by these "tricks" of nature will find thousands of useful and amazing pieces of information. Hundreds of observational experiments are suggested which require no special equipment. 200 illustrations; 42 photos. xvi + 362pp. 5⅜ x 8.   T196 Paperbound **$2.00**

*MATHEMATICS IN ACTION, O. G. Sutton. Everyone with a command of high school algebra will find this book one of the finest possible introductions to the application of mathematics to physical theory. Ballistics, numerical analysis, waves and wavelike phenomena, Fourier series, group concepts, fluid flow and aerodynamics, statistical measures, and meteorology are discussed with unusual clarity. Some calculus and differential equations theory is developed by the author for the reader's help in the more difficult sections. 88 figures. Index. viii + 236pp. 5⅜ x 8.   T440 Clothbound **$3.50**

SOAP-BUBBLES: THEIR COLOURS AND THE FORCES THAT MOULD THEM, C. V. Boys. For continuing popularity and validity as scientific primer, few books can match this volume of easily-followed experiments, explanations. Lucid exposition of complexities of liquid films, surface tension and related phenomena, bubbles' reaction to heat, motion, music, magnetic fields. Experiments with capillary attraction, soap bubbles on frames, composite bubbles, liquid cylinders and jets, bubbles other than soap, etc. Wonderful introduction to scientific method, natural laws that have many ramifications in areas of modern physics. Only complete edition in print. New Introduction by S. Z. Lewin, New York University. 83 illustrations; 1 full-page color plate. xii + 190pp. 5⅜ x 8½.   T542 Paperbound **$1.50**

THE STORY OF X-RAYS FROM RÖNTGEN TO ISOTOPES, A. R. Bleich, M.D. This book, by a member of the American College of Radiology, gives the scientific explanation of x-rays, their applications in medicine, industry and art, and their danger (and that of atmospheric radiation) to the individual and the species. You learn how radiation therapy is applied against cancer, how x-rays diagnose heart disease and other ailments, how they are used to examine mummies for information on diseases of early societies, and industrial materials for hidden weaknesses. 54 illustrations show x-rays of flowers, bones, stomach, gears with flaws, etc. 1st publication. Index. xix + 186pp. 5⅜ x 8. T622 Paperbound **$1.50**

SPINNING TOPS AND GYROSCOPIC MOTION, John Perry. A classic elementary text of the dynamics of rotation — the behavior and use of rotating bodies such as gyroscopes and tops. In simple, everyday English you are shown how quasi-rigidity is induced in discs of paper, smoke rings, chains, etc., by rapid motions; why a gyrostat falls and why a top rises; precession; how the earth's motion affects climate; and many other phenomena. Appendix on practical use of gyroscopes. 62 figures. 128pp. 5⅜ x 8. T416 Paperbound **$1.25**

SNOW CRYSTALS, W. A. Bentley, M. J. Humphreys. For almost 50 years W. A. Bentley photographed snow flakes in his laboratory in Jericho, Vermont; in 1931 the American Meteorological Society gathered together the best of his work, some 2400 photographs of snow flakes, plus a few ice flowers, windowpane frosts, dew, frozen rain, and other ice formations. Pictures were selected for beauty and scientific value. A very valuable work to anyone in meteorology, cryology; most interesting to layman; extremely useful for artist who wants beautiful, crystalline designs. All copyright free. Unabridged reprint of 1931 edition. 2453 illustrations. 227pp. 8 x 10½. T287 Paperbound **$3.25**

A DOVER SCIENCE SAMPLER, edited by George Barkin. A collection of brief, non-technical passages from 44 Dover Books Explaining Science for the enjoyment of the science-minded browser. Includes work of Bertrand Russell, Poincaré, Laplace, Max Born, Galileo, Newton; material on physics, mathematics, metallurgy, anatomy, astronomy, chemistry, etc. You will be fascinated by Martin Gardner's analysis of the sincere pseudo-scientist, Moritz's account of Newton's absentmindedness, Bernard's examples of human vivisection, etc. Illustrations from the Diderot Pictorial Encyclopedia and De Re Metallica. 64 pages. **FREE**

THE STORY OF ATOMIC THEORY AND ATOMIC ENERGY, J. G. Feinberg. A broader approach to subject of nuclear energy and its cultural implications than any other similar source. Very readable, informal, completely non-technical text. Begins with first atomic theory, 600 B.C. and carries you through the work of Mendelejeff, Röntgen, Madame Curie, to Einstein's equation and the A-bomb. New chapter goes through thermonuclear fission, binding energy, other events up to 1959. Radioactive decay and radiation hazards, future benefits, work of Bohr, moderns, hundreds more topics. "Deserves special mention . . . not only authoritative but thoroughly popular in the best sense of the word," Saturday Review. Formerly, "The Atom Story." Expanded with new chapter. Three appendixes. Index. 34 illustrations. vii + 243pp. 5⅜ x 8. T625 Paperbound **$2.00**

THE STRANGE STORY OF THE QUANTUM, AN ACCOUNT FOR THE GENERAL READER OF THE GROWTH OF IDEAS UNDERLYING OUR PRESENT ATOMIC KNOWLEDGE, B. Hoffmann. Presents lucidly and expertly, with barest amount of mathematics, the problems and theories which led to modern quantum physics. Dr. Hoffmann begins with the closing years of the 19th century, when certain trifling discrepancies were noticed, and with illuminating analogies and examples takes you through the brilliant concepts of Planck, Einstein, Pauli, Broglie, Bohr, Schroedinger, Heisenberg, Dirac, Sommerfeld, Feynman, etc. This edition includes a new, long postscript carrying the story through 1958. "Of the books attempting an account of the history and contents of our modern atomic physics which have come to my attention, this is the best," H. Margenau, Yale University, in "American Journal of Physics." 32 tables and line illustrations. Index. 275pp. 5⅜ x 8. T518 Paperbound **$1.75**

SPACE AND TIME, E. Borel. Written by a versatile mathematician of world renown with his customary lucidity and precision, this introduction to relativity for the layman presents scores of examples, analogies, and illustrations that open up new ways of thinking about space and time. It covers abstract geometry and geographical maps, continuity and topology, the propagation of light, the special theory of relativity, the general theory of relativity, theoretical researches, and much more. Mathematical notes. 2 Indexes. 4 Appendices. 15 figures. xvi + 243pp. 5⅜ x 8. T592 Paperbound **$1.75**

FROM EUCLID TO EDDINGTON: A STUDY OF THE CONCEPTIONS OF THE EXTERNAL WORLD, Sir Edmund Whittaker. A foremost British scientist traces the development of theories of natural philosophy from the western rediscovery of Euclid to Eddington, Einstein, Dirac, etc. The inadequacy of classical physics is contrasted with present day attempts to understand the physical world through relativity, non-Euclidean geometry, space curvature, wave mechanics, etc. 5 major divisions of examination: Space; Time and Movement; the Concepts of Classical Physics; the Concepts of Quantum Mechanics; the Eddington Universe. 212pp. 5⅜ x 8. T491 Paperbound **$1.35**

Nature

AN INTRODUCTION TO BIRD LIFE FOR BIRD WATCHERS, Aretas A. Saunders. Fine, readable introduction to birdwatching. Includes a great deal of basic information on about 160 different varieties of wild birds—elementary facts not easily found elsewhere. Complete guide to identification procedures, methods of observation, important habits of birds, finding nests, food, etc. "Could make bird watchers of readers who never suspected they were vulnerable to that particular virus," CHICAGO SUNDAY TRIBUNE. Unabridged, corrected edition. Bibliography. Index. 22 line drawings by D. D'Ostilio. Formerly "The Lives of Wild Birds." 256pp. 5⅜ x 8½.   **T1139 Paperbound $1.25**

LIFE HISTORIES OF NORTH AMERICAN BIRDS, Arthur Cleveland Bent. Bent's historic, all-encompassing series on North American birds, originally produced under the auspices of the Smithsonian Institution, now being republished in its entirety by Dover Publications. The twenty-volume collection forms the most comprehensive, most complete, most-used source of information in existence. Each study describes in detail the characteristics, range, distribution, habits, migratory patterns, courtship procedures, plumage, eggs, voice, enemies, etc. of the different species and subspecies of the birds that inhabit our continent, utilizing reports of hundreds of contemporary observers as well as the writings of the great naturalists of the past. Invaluable to the ornithologist, conservationist, amateur naturalist, and birdwatcher. All books in the series contain numerous photographs to provide handy guides for identification and study.

LIFE HISTORIES OF NORTH AMERICAN BIRDS OF PREY. Including hawks, eagles, falcons, buzzards, condors, owls, etc. Index. Bibliographies of 923 items. 197 full-page plates containing close to 400 photographs. Total of 907pp. 5⅜ x 8½.   Vol. I: T931 Paperbound **$2.50**
Vol. II: T932 Paperbound **$2.50**
The set Paperbound **$5.00**

LIFE HISTORIES OF NORTH AMERICAN SHORE BIRDS. Including 81 varieties of such birds as sandpipers, woodcocks, snipes, phalaropes, oyster catchers, and many others. Index for each volume. Bibliographies of 449 entries. 121 full-page plates including over 200 photographs. Total of 860 pp. 5⅜ x 8½.   Vol. I: T933 Paperbound **$2.35**
Vol. II: T934 Paperbound **$2.35**
The set Paperbound **$4.70**

LIFE HISTORIES OF NORTH AMERICAN WILD FOWL. Including 73 varieties of ducks, geese, mergansers, swans, etc. Index for each volume. Bibliographies of 268 items. 106 full-page plates containing close to 200 photographs. Total of 685pp. 5⅜ x 8½.
Vol. I: T285 Paperbound **$2.50**
Vol. II: T286 Paperbound **$2.50**
The set Paperbound **$5.00**

LIFE HISTORIES OF NORTH AMERICAN GULLS AND TERNS. 50 different varieties of gulls and terns. Index. Bibliography. 93 plates including 149 photographs. xii + 337pp. 5⅜ x 8½.
T1029 Paperbound $2.75

LIFE HISTORIES OF NORTH AMERICAN GALLINACEOUS BIRDS. Including partridge, quail, grouse, pheasant, pigeons, doves, and others. Index. Bibliography. 93 full-page plates including 170 photographs. xiii + 490pp. 5⅜ x 8½.   **T1028 Paperbound $2.75**

THE MALAY ARCHIPELAGO, Alfred Russel Wallace. The record of the explorations (8 years, 14,000 miles) of the Malay Archipelago by a great scientific observer. A contemporary of Darwin, Wallace independently arrived at the concept of evolution by natural selection, applied the new theories of evolution to later genetic discoveries, and made significant contributions to biology, zoology, and botany. This work is still one of the classics of natural history and travel. It contains the author's reports of the different native peoples of the islands, descriptions of the island groupings, his accounts of the animals, birds, and insects that flourished in this area. The reader is carried through strange lands, alien cultures, and new theories, and will share in an exciting, unrivalled travel experience. Unabridged reprint of the 1922 edition, with 62 drawings and maps. 3 appendices, one on cranial measurements. xvii + 515pp. 5⅜ x 8.   **T187 Paperbound $2.25**

THE TRAVELS OF WILLIAM BARTRAM, edited by Mark Van Doren. This famous source-book of American anthropology, natural history, geography is the record kept by Bartram in the 1770's, on travels through the wilderness of Florida, Georgia, the Carolinas. Containing accurate and beautiful descriptions of Indians, settlers, fauna, flora, it is one of the finest pieces of Americana ever written. Introduction by Mark Van Doren. 13 original illustrations. Index. 448pp. 5⅜ x 8.   **T13 Paperbound $2.00**

COMMON SPIDERS OF THE UNITED STATES, J. H. Emerton. Only non-technical, but thorough, reliable guide to spiders for the layman. Over 200 spiders from all parts of the country, arranged by scientific classification, are identified by shape and color, number of eyes, habitat and range, habits, etc. Full text, 501 line drawings and photographs, and valuable introduction explain webs, poisons, threads, capturing and preserving spiders, etc. Index. New synoptic key by S. W. Frost. xxiv + 225pp. 5⅜ x 8.   **T223 Paperbound $1.45**

Biological Sciences

AN INTRODUCTION TO GENETICS, A. H. Sturtevant and G. W. Beadle. A very thorough exposition of genetic analysis and the chromosome mechanics of higher organisms by two of the world's most renowned biologists, A. H. Sturtevant, one of the founders of modern genetics, and George Beadle, Nobel laureate in 1958. Does not concentrate on the biochemical approach, but rather more on observed data from experimental evidence and results . . . from Drosophila and other life forms. Some chapter titles: Sex chromosomes; Sex-Linkage; Autosomal Inheritance;; Chromosome Maps; Intra-Chromosomal Rearrangements; Inversions—and Incomplete Chromosomes; Translocations; Lethals; Mutations; Heterogeneous Populations; Genes and Phenotypes; The Determination and Differentiation of Sex; etc. Slightly corrected reprint of 1939 edition. New preface by Drs. Sturtevant and Beadle. 1 color plate. 126 figures. Bibliographies. Index. 391pp. 5⅜ x 8½.   S306 Paperbound **$2.00**

THE GENETICAL THEORY OF NATURAL SELECTION, R. A. Fisher. 2nd revised edition of a vital reviewing of Darwin's Selection Theory in terms of particulate inheritance, by one of the great authorities on experimental and theoretical genetics. Theory is stated in mathematical form. Special features of particulate inheritance are examined: evolution of dominance, maintenance of specific variability, mimicry and sexual selection, etc. 5 chapters on man and his special circumstances as a social animal. 16 photographs. Bibliography. Index. x + 310pp. 5⅜ x 8.   S466 Paperbound **$2.00**

THE ORIENTATION OF ANIMALS: KINESES, TAXES AND COMPASS REACTIONS, Gottfried S. Fraenkel and Donald L. Gunn. A basic work in the field of animal orientations. Complete, detailed survey of everything known in the subject up to 1940s, enlarged and revised to cover major developments to 1960. Analyses of simpler types of orientation are presented in Part I: kinesis, klinotaxis, tropotaxis, telotaxis, etc. Part II covers more complex reactions originating from temperature changes, gravity, chemical stimulation, etc. The two-light experiment and unilateral blinding are dealt with, as is the problem of determinism or volition in lower animals. The book has become the universally-accepted guide to all who deal with the subject—zoologists, biologists, psychologists, and the like. Second, enlarged edition, revised to 1960. Bibliography of over 500 items. 135 illustrations. Indices. xiii + 376pp. 5⅜ x 8½.   T786 Paperbound **$2.25**

THE BEHAVIOUR AND SOCIAL LIFE OF HONEYBEES, C. R. Ribbands. Definitive survey of all aspects of honeybee life and behavior; completely scientific in approach, but written in interesting, everyday language that both professionals and laymen will appreciate. Basic coverage of physiology, anatomy, sensory equipment; thorough account of honeybee behavior in the field (foraging activities, nectar and pollen gathering, how individuals find their way home and back to food areas, mating habits, etc.); details of communication in various field and hive situations. An extensive treatment of activities within the hive community—food sharing, wax production, comb building, swarming, the queen, her life and relationship with the workers, etc. A must for the beekeeper, natural historian, biologist, entomologist, social scientist, et al. "An indispensable reference," J. Hambleton, BEES. "Recommended in the strongest of terms," AMERICAN SCIENTIST. 9 plates. 66 figures. Indices. 693-item bibliography. 252pp. 5⅜ x 8½.   T1137 Paperbound **$2.00**

BIRD DISPLAY: AN INTRODUCTION TO THE STUDY OF BIRD PSYCHOLOGY, E. A. Armstrong. The standard work on bird display, based on extensive observation by the author and reports of other observers. This important contribution to comparative psychology covers the behavior and ceremonial rituals of hundreds of birds from gannet and heron to birds of paradise and king penguins. Chapters discuss such topics as the ceremonial of the gannet, ceremonial gaping, disablement reactions, the expression of emotions, the evolution and function of social ceremonies, social hierarchy in bird life, dances of birds and men, songs, etc. Free of technical terminology, this work will be equally interesting to psychologists and zoologists as well as bird lovers of all backgrounds. 32 photographic plates. New introduction by the author. List of scientific names of birds. Bibliography. 3-part index. 431pp. 5⅜ x 8½.   T1128 Paperbound **$2.00**

THE SPECIFICITY OF SEROLOGICAL REACTIONS, Karl Landsteiner. With a Chapter on Molecular Structure and Intermolecular Forces by Linus Pauling. Dr. Landsteiner, winner of the Nobel Prize in 1930 for the discovery of the human blood groups, devoted his life to fundamental research and played a leading role in the development of immunology. This authoritative study is an account of the experiments he and his colleagues carried out on antigens and serological reactions with simple compounds. Comprehensive coverage of the basic concepts of immunolgy includes such topics as: The Serological Specificity of Proteins, Antigens, Antibodies, Artificially Conjugated Antigens, Non-Protein Cell Substances such as polysaccharides, etc., Antigen-Antibody Reactions (Toxin Neutralization, Precipitin Reactions, Agglutination, etc.). Discussions of toxins, bacterial proteins, viruses, hormones, enzymes, etc. in the context of immunological phenomena. New introduction by Dr. Merrill Chase of the Rockefeller Institute. Extensive bibliography and bibliography of author's writings. Index. xviii + 330pp. 5⅜ x 8½.   S299 Paperbound **$2.00**

Puzzles, Mathematical Recreations

SYMBOLIC LOGIC and THE GAME OF LOGIC, Lewis Carroll. "Symbolic Logic" is not concerned with modern symbolic logic, but is instead a collection of over 380 problems posed with charm and imagination, using the syllogism, and a fascinating diagrammatic method of drawing conclusions. In "The Game of Logic" Carroll's whimsical imagination devises a logical game played with 2 diagrams and counters (included) to manipulate hundreds of tricky syllogisms. The final section, "Hit or Miss" is a lagniappe of 101 additional puzzles in the delightful Carroll manner. Until this reprint edition, both of these books were rarities costing up to $15 each. Symbolic Logic: Index. xxxi + 199pp. The Game of Logic: 96pp. 2 vols. bound as one. 5⅜ x 8.　　　　　　　　　　　　　　　　　T492 Paperbound **$1.75**

PILLOW PROBLEMS and A TANGLED TALE, Lewis Carroll. One of the rarest of all Carroll's works, "Pillow Problems" contains 72 original math puzzles, all typically ingenious. Particularly fascinating are Carroll's answers which remain exactly as he thought them out, reflecting his actual mental process. The problems in "A Tangled Tale" are in story form, originally appearing as a monthly magazine serial. Carroll not only gives the solutions, but uses answers sent in by readers to discuss wrong approaches and misleading paths, and grades them for insight. Both of these books were rarities until this edition, "Pillow Problems" costing up to $25, and "A Tangled Tale" $15. Pillow Problems: Preface and Introduction by Lewis Carroll. xx + 109pp. A Tangled Tale: 6 illustrations. 152pp. Two vols. bound as one. 5⅜ x 8.　　　　　　　　　　　　　　　　　T493 Paperbound **$1.75**

AMUSEMENTS IN MATHEMATICS, Henry Ernest Dudeney. The foremost British originator of mathematical puzzles is always intriguing, witty, and paradoxical in this classic, one of the largest collections of mathematical amusements. More than 430 puzzles, problems, and paradoxes. Mazes and games, problems on number manipulation, unicursal and other route problems, puzzles on measuring, weighing, packing, age, kinship, chessboards, joiners', crossing river, plane figure dissection, and many others. Solutions. More than 450 illustrations. vii + 258pp. 5⅜ x 8.　　　　　　　　　　　　　　　　　T473 Paperbound **$1.25**

THE CANTERBURY PUZZLES, Henry Dudeney. Chaucer's pilgrims set one another problems in story form. Also Adventures of the Puzzle Club, the Strange Escape of the King's Jester, the Monks of Riddlewell, the Squire's Christmas Puzzle Party, and others. All puzzles are original, based on dissecting plane figures, arithmetic, algebra, elementary calculus and other branches of mathematics, and purely logical ingenuity. "The limit of ingenuity and intricacy," The Observer. Over 110 puzzles. Full Solutions. 150 illustrations. vii + 225pp. 5⅜ x 8.　　　　　　　　　　　　　　　　　T474 Paperbound **$1.25**

MATHEMATICAL EXCURSIONS, H. A. Merrill. Even if you hardly remember your high school math, you'll enjoy the 90 stimulating problems contained in this book and you will come to understand a great many mathematical principles with surprisingly little effort. Many useful shortcuts and diversions not generally known are included: division by inspection, Russian peasant multiplication, memory systems for pi, building odd and even magic squares, square roots by geometry, dyadic systems, and many more. Solutions to difficult problems. 50 illustrations. 145pp. 5⅜ x 8.　　　　　　　　　　　　　　　　　T350 Paperbound **$1.25**

MAGIC SQUARES AND CUBES, W. S. Andrews. Only book-length treatment in English, a thorough non-technical description and analysis. Here are nasik, overlapping, pandiagonal, serrated squares; magic circles, cubes, spheres, rhombuses. Try your hand at 4-dimensional magical figures! Much unusual folklore and tradition included. High school algebra is sufficient. 754 diagrams and illustrations. viii + 419pp. 5⅜ x 8.　　　　　　　　　　　　　　　T658 Paperbound **$1.85**

CALIBAN'S PROBLEM BOOK: MATHEMATICAL, INFERENTIAL AND CRYPTOGRAPHIC PUZZLES, H. Phillips (Caliban), S. T. Shovelton, G. S. Marshall. 105 ingenious problems by the greatest living creator of puzzles based on logic and inference. Rigorous, modern, piquant; reflecting their author's unusual personality, these intermediate and advanced puzzles all involve the ability to reason clearly through complex situations; some call for mathematical knowledge, ranging from algebra to number theory. Solutions. xi + 180pp. 5⅜ x 8.　　　　　　　　　　　　　　　　　T736 Paperbound **$1.50**

MATHEMATICAL PUZZLES FOR BEGINNERS AND ENTHUSIASTS, G. Mott-Smith. 188 mathematical puzzles based on algebra, dissection of plane figures, permutations, and probability, that will test and improve your powers of inference and interpretation. The Odic Force, The Spider's Cousin, Ellipse Drawing, theory and strategy of card and board games like tit-tat-toe, go moku, salvo, and many others. 100 pages of detailed mathematical explanations. Appendix of primes, square roots, etc. 135 illustrations. 2nd revised edition. 248pp. 5⅜ x 8.　　　　　　　　　　　　　　　　　T198 Paperbound **$1.25**

MATHEMAGIC, MAGIC PUZZLES, AND GAMES WITH NUMBERS, R. V. Heath. More than 60 new puzzles and stunts based on the properties of numbers. Easy techniques for multiplying large numbers mentally, revealing hidden numbers magically, finding the date of any day in any year, and dozens more. Over 30 pages devoted to magic squares, triangles, cubes, circles, etc. Edited by J. S. Meyer. 76 illustrations. 128pp. 5⅜ x 8.　　　　　　　　　　　　　　T110 Paperbound **$1.00**

THE BOOK OF MODERN PUZZLES, G. L. Kaufman. A completely new series of puzzles as fascinating as crossword and deduction puzzles but based upon different principles and techniques. Simple 2-minute teasers, word labyrinths, design and pattern puzzles, logic and observation puzzles — over 150 braincrackers. Answers to all problems. 116 illustrations. 192pp. 5⅜ x 8.
T143 Paperbound **$1.00**

NEW WORD PUZZLES, G. L. Kaufman. 100 ENTIRELY NEW puzzles based on words and their combinations that will delight crossword puzzle, Scrabble and Jotto fans. Chess words, based on the moves of the chess king; design-onyms, symmetrical designs made of synonyms; rhymed double-crostics; syllable sentences; addle letter anagrams; alphagrams; linkograms; and many others all brand new. Full solutions. Space to work problems. 196 figures. vi + 122pp. 5⅜ x 8.
T344 Paperbound **$1.00**

MAZES AND LABYRINTHS: A BOOK OF PUZZLES, W. Shepherd. Mazes, formerly associated with mystery and ritual, are still among the most intriguing of intellectual puzzles. This is a novel and different collection of 50 amusements that embody the principle of the maze: mazes in the classical tradition; 3-dimensional, ribbon, and Möbius-strip mazes; hidden messages; spatial arrangements; etc.—almost all built on amusing story situations. 84 illustrations. Essay on maze psychology. Solutions. xv + 122pp. 5⅜ x 8.
T731 Paperbound **$1.00**

MAGIC TRICKS & CARD TRICKS, W. Jonson. Two books bound as one. 52 tricks with cards, 37 tricks with coins, bills, eggs, smoke, ribbons, slates, etc. Details on presentation, misdirection, and routining will help you master such famous tricks as the Changing Card, Card in the Pocket, Four Aces, Coin Through the Hand, Bill in the Egg, Afghan Bands, and over 75 others. If you follow the lucid exposition and key diagrams carefully, you will finish these two books with an astonishing mastery of magic. 106 figures. 224pp. 5⅜ x 8. T909 Paperbound **$1.00**

PANORAMA OF MAGIC, Milbourne Christopher. A profusely illustrated history of stage magic, a unique selection of prints and engravings from the author's private collection of magic memorabilia, the largest of its kind. Apparatus, stage settings and costumes; ingenious ads distributed by the performers and satiric broadsides passed around in the streets ridiculing pompous showmen; programs; decorative souvenirs. The lively text, by one of America's foremost professional magicians, is full of anecdotes about almost legendary wizards: Dede, the Egyptian; Philadelphia, the wonder-worker; Robert-Houdin, "the father of modern magic;" Harry Houdini; scores more. Altogether a pleasure package for anyone interested in magic, stage setting and design, ethnology, psychology, or simply in unusual people. A Dover original. 295 illustrations; 8 in full color. Index. viii + 216pp. 8⅜ x 11¼.
T774 Paperbound **$2.25**

HOUDINI ON MAGIC, Harry Houdini. One of the greatest magicians of modern times explains his most prized secrets. How locks are picked, with illustrated picks and skeleton keys; how a girl is sawed into twins; how to walk through a brick wall — Houdini's explanations of 44 stage tricks with many diagrams. Also included is a fascinating discussion of great magicians of the past and the story of his fight against fraudulent mediums and spiritualists. Edited by W.B. Gibson and M.N. Young. Bibliography. 155 figures, photos. xv + 280pp. 5⅜ x 8.
T384 Paperbound **$1.50**

MATHEMATICS, MAGIC AND MYSTERY, Martin Gardner. Why do card tricks work? How do magicians perform astonishing mathematical feats? How is stage mind-reading possible? This is the first book length study explaining the application of probability, set theory, theory of numbers, topology, etc., to achieve many startling tricks. Non-technical, accurate, detailed! 115 sections discuss tricks with cards, dice, coins, knots, geometrical vanishing illusions, how a Curry square "demonstrates" that the sum of the parts may be greater than the whole, and dozens of others. No sleight of hand necessary! 135 illustrations. xii + 174pp. 5⅜ x 8.
T335 Paperbound **$1.00**

EASY-TO-DO ENTERTAINMENTS AND DIVERSIONS WITH COINS, CARDS, STRING, PAPER AND MATCHES, R. M. Abraham. Over 300 tricks, games and puzzles will provide young readers with absorbing fun. Sections on card games; paper-folding; tricks with coins, matches and pieces of string; games for the agile; toy-making from common household objects; mathematical recreations; and 50 miscellaneous pastimes. Anyone in charge of groups of youngsters, including hard-pressed parents, and in need of suggestions on how to keep children sensibly amused and quietly content will find this book indispensable. Clear, simple text, copious number of delightful line drawings and illustrative diagrams. Originally titled "Winter Nights Entertainments." Introduction by Lord Baden Powell. 329 illustrations. v + 186pp. 5⅜ x 8½.
T921 Paperbound **$1.00**

STRING FIGURES AND HOW TO MAKE THEM, Caroline Furness Jayne. 107 string figures plus variations selected from the best primitive and modern examples developed by Navajo, Apache, pygmies of Africa, Eskimo, in Europe, Australia, China, etc. The most readily understandable, easy-to-follow book in English on perennially popular recreation. Crystal-clear exposition; step-by-step diagrams. Everyone from kindergarten children to adults looking for unusual diversion will be endlessly amused. Index. Bibliography. Introduction by A. C. Haddon. 17 full-page plates. 960 illustrations. xxiii + 401pp. 5⅜ x 8½.
T152 Paperbound **$2.00**

Entertainments, Humor

ODDITIES AND CURIOSITIES OF WORDS AND LITERATURE, C. Bombaugh, edited by M. Gardner.
The largest collection of idiosyncratic prose and poetry techniques in English, a legendary
work in the curious and amusing bypaths of literary recreations and the play technique in
literature—so important in modern works. Contains alphabetic poetry, acrostics, palindromes,
scissors verse, centos, emblematic poetry, famous literary puns, hoaxes, notorious slips of
the press, hilarious mistranslations, and much more. Revised and enlarged with modern
material by Martin Gardner. 368pp. 5⅜ x 8.   T759 Paperbound **$1.75**

A NONSENSE ANTHOLOGY, collected by Carolyn Wells. 245 of the best nonsense verses ever
written, including nonsense puns, absurd arguments, mock epics and sagas, nonsense ballads,
odes, "sick" verses, dog-Latin verses, French nonsense verses, songs. By Edward Lear,
Lewis Carroll, Gelett Burgess, W. S. Gilbert, Hilaire Belloc, Peter Newell, Oliver Herford, etc.,
83 writers in all plus over four score anonymous nonsense verses. A special section of
limericks, plus famous nonsense such as Carroll's "Jabberwocky" and Lear's "The Jumblies"
and much excellent verse virtually impossible to locate elsewhere. For 50 years considered
the best anthology available. Index of first lines specially prepared for this edition.
Introduction by Carolyn Wells. 3 indexes: Title, Author, First lines. xxxiii + 279pp.
                                                          T499 Paperbound **$1.50**

**THE BAD CHILD'S BOOK OF BEASTS, MORE BEASTS FOR WORSE CHILDREN, and A MORAL ALPHA-
BET, H. Belloc.** Hardly an anthology of humorous verse has appeared in the last 50 years
without at least a couple of these famous nonsense verses. But one must see the entire volumes—with all the delightful original illustrations by Sir Basil Blackwood—to appreciate
fully Belloc's charming and witty verses that play so subacidly on the platitudes of life and
morals that beset his day—and ours. A great humor classic. Three books in one. Total of
157pp. 5⅜ x 8.   T749 Paperbound **$1.00**

THE DEVIL'S DICTIONARY, Ambrose Bierce. Sardonic and irreverent barbs puncturing the
pomposities and absurdities of American politics, business, religion, literature, and arts,
by the country's greatest satirist in the classic tradition. Epigrammatic as Shaw, piercing
as Swift, American as Mark Twain, Will Rogers, and Fred Allen, Bierce will always remain
the favorite of a small coterie of enthusiasts, and of writers and speakers whom he supplies
with "some of the most gorgeous witticisms of the English language" (H. L. Mencken).
Over 1000 entries in alphabetical order. 144pp. 5⅜ x 8.   T487 Paperbound **$1.00**

THE PURPLE COW AND OTHER NONSENSE, Gelett Burgess. The best of Burgess's early nonsense,
selected from the first edition of the "Burgess Nonsense Book." Contains many of his most
unusual and truly awe-inspiring pieces: 36 nonsense quatrains, the Poems of Patagonia, Alpha-
bet of Famous Goops, and the other hilarious (and rare) adult nonsense that place him in the
forefront of American humorists. All pieces are accompanied by the original Burgess illustrations. 123 illustrations. xiii + 113pp. 5⅜ x 8.   T772 Paperbound **$1.00**

**MY PIOUS FRIENDS AND DRUNKEN COMPANIONS and MORE PIOUS FRIENDS AND DRUNKEN
COMPANIONS, Frank Shay.** Folksingers, amateur and professional, and everyone who loves
singing: here, available for the first time in 30 years, is this valued collection of 132 ballads,
blues, vaudeville numbers, drinking songs, sea chanties, comedy songs. Songs of pre-Beatnik
Bohemia; songs from all over America, England, France, Australia; the great songs of the
Naughty Nineties and early twentieth-century America. Over a third with music. Woodcuts
by John Held, Jr. convey perfectly the brash insouciance of an era of rollicking unabashed
song. 12 illustrations by John Held, Jr. Two indexes (Titles and First lines and Choruses).
Introductions by the author. Two volumes bound as one. Total of xvi + 235pp. 5⅜ x 8½.
                                                          T946 Paperbound **$1.25**

HOW TO TELL THE BIRDS FROM THE FLOWERS, R. W. Wood. How not to confuse a carrot with
a parrot, a grape with an ape, a puffin with nuffin. Delightful drawings, clever puns, absurd
little poems point out far-fetched resemblances in nature. The author was a leading
physicist. Introduction by Margaret Wood White. 106 illus. 60pp. 5⅜ x 8.
                                                          T523 Paperbound **75¢**

PECK'S BAD BOY AND HIS PA, George W. Peck. The complete edition, containing both
volumes, of one of the most widely read American humor books. The endless ingenious
pranks played by bad boy "Hennery" on his pa and the grocery man, the outraged pomposity
of Pa, the perpetual ridiculing of middle class institutions, are as entertaining today as they
were in 1883. No pale sophistications or subtleties, but rather humor vigorous, raw, earthy,
imaginative, and, as folk humor often is, sadistic. This peculiarly fascinating book is also
valuable to historians and students of American culture as a portrait of an age. 100
original illustrations by True Williams. Introduction by E. F. Bleiler. 347pp. 5⅜ x 8.
                                                          T497 Paperbound **$1.50**

THE HUMOROUS VERSE OF LEWIS CARROLL. Almost every poem Carroll ever wrote, the largest collection ever published, including much never published elsewhere: 150 parodies, burlesques, riddles, ballads, acrostics, etc., with 130 original illustrations by Tenniel, Carroll, and others. "Addicts will be grateful . . . there is nothing for the faithful to do but sit down and fall to the banquet," N. Y. Times. Index to first lines. xiv + 446pp. 5⅜ x 8.

T654 Paperbound **$2.00**

DIVERSIONS AND DIGRESSIONS OF LEWIS CARROLL. A major new treasure for Carroll fans! Rare privately published humor, fantasy, puzzles, and games by Carroll at his whimsical best, with a new vein of frank satire. Includes many new mathematical amusements and recreations, among them the fragmentary Part III of "Curiosa Mathematica." Contains "The Rectory Umbrella," "The New Belfry," "The Vision of the Three T's," and much more. New 32-page supplement of rare photographs taken by Carroll. x + 375pp. 5⅜ x 8.

T732 Paperbound **$2.00**

THE COMPLETE NONSENSE OF EDWARD LEAR. This is the only complete edition of this master of gentle madness available at a popular price. A BOOK OF NONSENSE, NONSENSE SONGS, MORE NONSENSE SONGS AND STORIES in their entirety with all the old favorites that have delighted children and adults for years. The Dong With A Luminous Nose, The Jumblies, The Owl and the Pussycat, and hundreds of other bits of wonderful nonsense. 214 limericks, 3 sets of Nonsense Botany, 5 Nonsense Alphabets, 546 drawings by Lear himself, and much more. 320pp. 5⅜ x 8.

T167 Paperbound **$1.00**

THE MELANCHOLY LUTE, The Humorous Verse of Franklin P. Adams ("FPA"). The author's own selection of light verse, drawn from thirty years of FPA's column, "The Conning Tower," syndicated all over the English-speaking world. Witty, perceptive, literate, these ninety-six poems range from parodies of other poets, Millay, Longfellow, Edgar Guest, Kipling, Masefield, etc., and free and hilarious translations of Horace and other Latin poets, to satiric comments on fabled American institutions—the New York Subways, preposterous ads, suburbanites, sensational journalism, etc. They reveal with vigor and clarity the humor, integrity and restraint of a wise and gentle American satirist. Introduction by Robert Hutchinson. vi + 122pp. 5⅜ x 8½.

T108 Paperbound **$1.00**

SINGULAR TRAVELS, CAMPAIGNS, AND ADVENTURES OF BARON MUNCHAUSEN, R. E. Raspe, with 90 illustrations by Gustave Doré. The first edition in over 150 years to reestablish the deeds of the Prince of Liars exactly as Raspe first recorded them in 1785—the genuine Baron Munchausen, one of the most popular personalities in English literature. Included also are the best of the many sequels, written by other hands. Introduction on Raspe by J. Carswell. Bibliography of early editions. xliv + 192pp. 5⅜ x 8.

T698 Paperbound **$1.25**

THE WIT AND HUMOR OF OSCAR WILDE, ed. by Alvin Redman. Wilde at his most brilliant, in 1000 epigrams exposing weaknesses and hypocrisies of "civilized" society. Divided into 49 categories—sin, wealth, women, America, etc.—to aid writers, speakers. Includes excerpts from his trials, books, plays, criticism. Formerly "The Epigrams of Oscar Wilde." Introduction by Vyvyan Holland, Wilde's only living son. Introductory essay by editor. 260pp. 5⅜ x 8.

T602 Paperbound **$1.00**

MAX AND MORITZ, Wilhelm Busch. Busch is one of the great humorists of all time, as well as the father of the modern comic strip. This volume, translated by H. A. Klein and other hands, contains the perennial favorite "Max and Moritz" (translated by C. T. Brooks), Plisch and Plum, Das Rabennest, Eispeter, and seven other whimsical, sardonic, jovial, diabolical cartoon and verse stories. Lively English translations parallel the original German. This work has delighted millions since it first appeared in the 19th century, and is guaranteed to please almost anyone. Edited by H. A. Klein, with an afterword. x + 205pp. 5⅝ x 8½.

T181 Paperbound **$1.25**

HYPOCRITICAL HELENA, Wilhelm Busch. A companion volume to "Max and Moritz," with the title piece (Die Fromme Helena) and 10 other highly amusing cartoon and verse stories, all newly translated by H. A. Klein and M. C. Klein: Adventure on New Year's Eve (Abenteuer in der Neujahrsnacht), Hangover on the Morning after New Year's Eve (Der Katzenjammer am Neujahrsmorgen), etc. English and German in parallel columns. Hours of pleasure, also a fine language aid. x + 205pp. 5⅝ x 8½.

T184 Paperbound **$1.00**

THE BEAR THAT WASN'T, Frank Tashlin. What does it mean? Is it simply delightful wry humor, or a charming story of a bear who wakes up in the midst of a factory, or a satire on Big Business, or an existential cartoon-story of the human condition, or a symbolization of the struggle between conformity and the individual? New York Herald Tribune said of the first edition: ". . . a fable for grownups that will be fun for children. Sit down with the book and get your own bearings." Long an underground favorite with readers of all ages and opinions. v + 51pp. Illustrated. 5⅜ x 8½.

T939 Paperbound **$1.00**

RUTHLESS RHYMES FOR HEARTLESS HOMES and MORE RUTHLESS RHYMES FOR HEARTLESS HOMES, Harry Graham ("Col. D. Streamer"). Two volumes of Little Willy and 48 other poetic disasters. A bright, new reprint of oft-quoted, never forgotten, devastating humor by a precursor of today's "sick" joke school. For connoisseurs of wicked, wacky humor and all who delight in the comedy of manners. Original drawings are a perfect complement. 61 illustrations. Index. vi + 69pp. Two vols. bound as one. 5⅜ x 8½.

T930 Paperbound **75¢**

Say It language phrase books

These handy phrase books (128 to 196 pages each) make grammatical drills unnecessary for an elementary knowledge of a spoken foreign language. Covering most matters of travel and everyday life each volume contains:

Over 1000 phrases and sentences in immediately useful forms — foreign language plus English.

Modern usage designed for Americans. Specific phrases like, "Give me small change," and "Please call a taxi."

Simplified phonetic transcription you will be able to read at sight.

The only completely indexed phrase books on the market.

Covers scores of important situations: — Greetings, restaurants, sightseeing, useful expressions, etc.

These books are prepared by native linguists who are professors at Columbia, N.Y.U., Fordham and other great universities. Use them independently or with any other book or record course. They provide a supplementary living element that most other courses lack. Individual volumes in:

Russian 75¢	Italian 75¢	Spanish 75¢	German 75¢
Hebrew 75¢	Danish 75¢	Japanese 75¢	Swedish 75¢
Dutch 75¢	Esperanto 75¢	Modern Greek 75¢	Portuguese 75¢
Norwegian 75¢	Polish 75¢	French 75¢	Yiddish 75¢
Turkish 75¢		English for German-speaking people 75¢	
English for Italian-speaking people 75¢		English for Spanish-speaking people 75¢	

Large clear type. 128-196 pages each. 3½ x 5¼. Sturdy paper binding.

Listen and Learn language records

LISTEN & LEARN is the only language record course designed especially to meet your travel and everyday needs. It is available in separate sets for FRENCH, SPANISH, GERMAN, JAPANESE, RUSSIAN, MODERN GREEK, PORTUGUESE, ITALIAN and HEBREW, and each set contains three 33⅓ rpm long-playing records—1½ hours of recorded speech by eminent native speakers who are professors at Columbia, New York University, Queens College.

Check the following special features found only in LISTEN & LEARN:

- **Dual-language recording. 812 selected phrases and sentences, over 3200 words,** spoken first in English, then in their foreign language equivalents. A suitable pause follows each foreign phrase, allowing you time to repeat the expression. You learn by unconscious assimilation.

- **128 to 206-page manual** contains everything on the records, plus a simple phonetic pronunciation guide.

- **Indexed for convenience. The only set on the market** that is completely indexed. No more puzzling over where to find the phrase you need. Just look in the rear of the manual.

- **Practical.** No time wasted on material you can find in any grammar. LISTEN & LEARN covers central core material with phrase approach. Ideal for the person with limited learning time.

- **Living, modern expressions,** not found in other courses. Hygienic products, modern equipment, shopping—expressions used every day, like "nylon" and "air-conditioned."

- **Limited objective.** Everything you learn, no matter where you stop, is immediately useful. You have to finish other courses, wade through grammar and vocabulary drill, before they help you.

- **High-fidelity recording.** LISTEN & LEARN records equal in clarity and surface-silence any record on the market costing up to $6.

"Excellent . . . the spoken records . . . impress me as being among the very best on the market," **Prof. Mario Pei,** Dept. of Romance Languages, Columbia University. "Inexpensive and well-done . . . it would make an ideal present," CHICAGO SUNDAY TRIBUNE. "More genuinely helpful than anything of its kind which I have previously encountered," **Sidney Clark,** well-known author of "ALL THE BEST" travel books.

UNCONDITIONAL GUARANTEE. Try LISTEN & LEARN, then return it within 10 days for full refund if you are not satisfied.

Each set contains three twelve-inch 33⅓ records, manual, and album.

SPANISH	the set $5.95	GERMAN	the set $5.95
FRENCH	the set $5.95	ITALIAN	the set $5.95
RUSSIAN	the set $5.95	JAPANESE	the set $6.95
PORTUGUESE	the set $5.95	MODERN GREEK	the set $5.95
MODERN HEBREW	the set $5.95		

Americana

THE EYES OF DISCOVERY, J. Bakeless. A vivid reconstruction of how—unspoiled America appeared to the first white men. Authentic and enlightening accounts of Hudson's landing in New York, Coronado's trek through the Southwest; scores of explorers, settlers, trappers, soldiers. America's pristine flora, fauna, and Indians in every region and state in fresh and unusual new aspects. "A fascinating view of what the land was like before the first highway went through," Time. 68 contemporary illustrations, 39 newly added in this edition. Index. Bibliography. x + 500pp. 5⅜ x 8.   T761 Paperbound **$2.25**

AUDUBON AND HIS JOURNALS, J. J. Audubon. A collection of fascinating accounts of Europe and America in the early 1800's through Audubon's own eyes. Includes the Missouri River Journals —an eventful trip through America's untouched heartland, the Labrador Journals, the European Journals, the famous "Episodes", and other rare Audubon material, including the descriptive chapters from the original letterpress edition of the "Ornithological Studies", omitted in all later editions. Indispensable for ornithologists, naturalists, and all lovers of Americana and adventure. 70-page biography by Audubon's granddaughter. 38 illustrations. Index. Total of 1106pp. 5⅜ x 8.   T675 Vol I Paperbound **$2.25**
                                    T676 Vol II Paperbound **$2.25**
                                    The set **$4.50**

TRAVELS OF WILLIAM BARTRAM, edited by Mark Van Doren. The first inexpensive illustrated edition of one of the 18th century's most delightful books is an excellent source of first-hand material on American geography, anthropology, and natural history. Many descriptions of early Indian tribes are our only source of information on them prior to the infiltration of the white man. "The mind of a scientist with the soul of a poet," John Livingston Lowes. 13 original illustrations and maps. Edited with an introduction by Mark Van Doren. 448pp. 5⅜ x 8.
                                    T13 Paperbound **$2.25**

GARRETS AND PRETENDERS: A HISTORY OF BOHEMIANISM IN AMERICA, A. Parry. The colorful and fantastic history of American Bohemianism from Poe to Kerouac. This is the only complete record of hoboes, cranks, starving poets, and suicides. Here are Pfaff, Whitman, Crane, Bierce, Pound, and many others. New chapters by the author and by H. T. Moore bring this thorough and well-documented history down to the Beatniks. "An excellent account," N. Y. Times. Scores of cartoons, drawings, and caricatures. Bibliography. Index. xxviii + 421pp. 5⅝ x 8⅜.   T708 Paperbound **$1.95**

THE EXPLORATION OF THE COLORADO RIVER AND ITS CANYONS, J. W. Powell. The thrilling first-hand account of the expedition that filled in the last white space on the map of the United States. Rapids, famine, hostile Indians, and mutiny are among the perils encountered as the unknown Colorado Valley reveals its secrets. This is the only uncut version of Major Powell's classic of exploration that has been printed in the last 60 years. Includes later reflections and subsequent expedition. 250 illustrations, new map. 400pp. 5⅝ x 8⅜.
                                    T94 Paperbound **$2.25**

THE JOURNAL OF HENRY D. THOREAU, Edited by Bradford Torrey and Francis H. Allen. Henry Thoreau is not only one of the most important figures in American literature and social thought; his voluminous journals (from which his books emerged as selections and crystallizations) constitute both the longest, most sensitive record of personal internal development and a most penetrating description of a historical moment in American culture. This present set, which was first issued in fourteen volumes, contains Thoreau's entire journals from 1837 to 1862, with the exception of the lost years which were found only recently. We are reissuing it, complete and unabridged, with a new introduction by Walter Harding, Secretary of the Thoreau Society. Fourteen volumes reissued in two volumes. Foreword by Henry Seidel Canby. Total of 1888pp. 8⅜ x 12¼.   T312-3 Two volume set, Clothbound **$22.50**

GAMES AND SONGS OF AMERICAN CHILDREN, collected by William Wells Newell. A remarkable collection of 190 games that accompany many of them; cross references to show similarities, differences among them; variations; musical notation for 38 songs. Textual discussions show relations with folk-drama and other aspects of folk tradition. Grouped into categories for ready comparative study: Love-games, histories, playing at work, human life, bird and beast, mythology, guessing-games, etc. New introduction covers relations of songs and dances to timeless heritage of folklore, biographical sketch of Newell, other pertinent data. A good source of inspiration for those in charge of groups of children and a valuable reference for anthropologists, sociologists, psychiatrists. Introduction by Carl Withers. New indexes of first lines, games. 5⅜ x 8½. xii + 242pp.   T354 Paperbound **$2.00**

Art, History of Art, Antiques, Graphic Arts, Handcrafts

ART STUDENTS' ANATOMY, E. J. Farris. Outstanding art anatomy that uses chiefly living objects for its illustrations. 71 photos of undraped men, women, children are accompanied by carefully labeled matching sketches to illustrate the skeletal system, articulations and movements, bony landmarks, the muscular system, skin, fasciae, fat, etc. 9 x-ray photos show movement of joints. Undraped models are shown in such actions as serving in tennis, drawing a bow in archery, playing football, dancing, preparing to spring and to dive. Also discussed and illustrated are proportions, age and sex differences, the anatomy of the smile, etc. 8 plates by the great early 18th century anatomic illustrator Siegfried Albinus are also included. Glossary. 158 figures, 7 in color. x + 159pp. 5⅝ x 8⅜.   T744 Paperbound **$1.50**

AN ATLAS OF ANATOMY FOR ARTISTS, F Schider. A new 3rd edition of this standard text enlarged by 52 new illustrations of hands, anatomical studies by Cloquet, and expressive life studies of the body by Barcsay. 189 clear, detailed plates offer you precise information of impeccable accuracy. 29 plates show all aspects of the skeleton, with closeups of special areas, while 54 full-page plates, mostly in two colors, give human musculature as seen from four different points of view, with cutaways for important portions of the body. 14 full-page plates provide photographs of hand forms, eyelids, female breasts, and indicate the location of muscles upon models. 59 additional plates show how great artists of the past utilized human anatomy. They reproduce sketches and finished work by such artists as Michelangelo, Leonardo da Vinci, Goya, and 15 others. This is a lifetime reference work which will be one of the most important books in any artist's library. "The standard reference tool," AMERICAN LIBRARY ASSOCIATION. "Excellent," AMERICAN ARTIST. Third enlarged edition. 189 plates, 647 illustrations. xxvi + 192pp. 7⅞ x 10⅝.   T241 Clothbound **$6.00**

AN ATLAS OF ANIMAL ANATOMY FOR ARTISTS, W. Ellenberger, H. Baum, H. Dittrich. The largest, richest animal anatomy for artists available in English. 99 detailed anatomical plates of such animals as the horse, dog, cat, lion, deer, seal, kangaroo, flying squirrel, cow, bull, goat, monkey, hare, and bat. Surface features are clearly indicated, while progressive beneath-the-skin pictures show musculature, tendons, and bone structure. Rest and action are exhibited in terms of musculature and skeletal structure and detailed cross-sections are given for heads and important features. The animals chosen are representative of specific families so that a study of these anatomies will provide knowledge of hundreds of related species. "Highly recommended as one of the very few books on the subject worthy of being used as an authoritative guide," DESIGN. "Gives a fundamental knowledge," AMERICAN ARTIST. Second revised, enlarged edition with new plates from Cuvier, Stubbs, etc. 288 illustrations. 153pp. 11⅜ x 9.   T82 Clothbound **$6.00**

THE HUMAN FIGURE IN MOTION, Eadweard Muybridge. The largest selection in print of Muybridge's famous high-speed action photos of the human figure in motion. 4789 photographs illustrate 162 different actions: men, women, children—mostly undraped—are shown walking, running, carrying various objects, sitting, lying down, climbing, throwing, arising, and performing over 150 other actions. Some actions are shown in as many as 150 photographs each. All in all there are more than 500 action strips in this enormous volume, series shots taken at shutter speeds of as high as 1/6000th of a second! These are not posed shots, but true stopped motion. They show bone and muscle in situations that the human eye is not fast enough to capture. Earlier, smaller editions of these prints have brought $40 and more on the out-of-print market. "A must for artists," ART IN FOCUS. "An unparalleled dictionary of action for all artists," AMERICAN ARTIST. 390 full-page plates, with 4789 photographs. Printed on heavy glossy stock. Reinforced binding with headbands. xxi + 390pp. 7⅞ x 10⅝.   T204 Clothbound **$10.00**

ANIMALS IN MOTION, Eadweard Muybridge. This is the largest collection of animal action photos in print. 34 different animals (horses, mules, oxen, goats, camels, pigs, cats, guanacos, lions, gnus, deer, monkeys, eagles—and 21 others) in 132 characteristic actions. The horse alone is shown in more than 40 different actions. All 3919 photographs are taken in series at speeds up to 1/6000th of a second. The secrets of leg motion, spinal patterns, head movements, strains and contortions shown nowhere else are captured. You will see exactly how a lion sets his foot down; how an elephant's knees are like a human's—and how they differ; the position of a kangaroo's legs in mid-leap; how an ostrich's head bobs; details of the flight of birds—and thousands of facets of motion only the fastest cameras can catch. Photographed from domestic animals and animals in the Philadelphia zoo, it contains neither semiposed artificial shots nor distorted telephoto shots taken under adverse conditions. Artists, biologists, decorators, cartoonists, will find this book indispensable for understanding animals in motion. "A really marvelous series of plates," NATURE (London). "The dry plate's most spectacular early use was by Eadweard Muybridge," LIFE. 3919 photographs; 380 full pages of plates. 440pp. Printed on heavy glossy paper. Deluxe binding with headbands. 7⅞ x 10⅝.   T203 Clothbound **$10.00**

CATALOGUE OF DOVER BOOKS

THE AUTOBIOGRAPHY OF AN IDEA, Louis Sullivan. The pioneer architect whom Frank Lloyd Wright called "the master" reveals an acute sensitivity to social forces and values in this passionately honest account. He records the crystallization of his opinions and theories, the growth of his organic theory of architecture that still influences American designers and architects, contemporary ideas, etc. This volume contains the first appearance of 34 full-page plates of his finest architecture. Unabridged reissue of 1924 edition. New introduction by R. M. Line. Index. xiv + 335pp. 5⅜ x 8.　　　　　　　　　　T281 Paperbound **$2.00**

THE DRAWINGS OF HEINRICH KLEY. The first uncut republication of both of Kley's devastating sketchbooks, which first appeared in pre-World War I Germany. One of the greatest cartoonists and social satirists of modern times, his exuberant and iconoclastic fantasy and his extraordinary technique place him in the great tradition of Bosch, Breughel, and Goya, while his subject matter has all the immediacy and tension of our century. 200 drawings. viii + 128pp. 7¾ x 10¾.　　　　　　　　　　T24 Paperbound **$1.85**

MORE DRAWINGS BY HEINRICH KLEY. All the sketches from Leut' Und Viecher (1912) and Sammel-Album (1923) not included in the previous Dover edition of Drawings. More of the bizarre, mercilessly iconoclastic sketches that shocked and amused on their original publication. Nothing was too sacred, no one too eminent for satirization by this imaginative, individual and accomplished master cartoonist. A total of 158 illustrations. lv + 104pp. 7¾ x 10¾.　　　　　　　　　　T41 Paperbound **$1.85**

PINE FURNITURE OF EARLY NEW ENGLAND, R. H. Kettell. A rich understanding of one of America's most original folk arts that collectors of antiques, interior decorators, craftsmen, woodworkers, and everyone interested in American history and art will find fascinating and immensely useful. 413 illustrations of more than 300 chairs, benches, racks, beds, cupboards, mirrors, shelves, tables, and other furniture will show all the simple beauty and character of early New England furniture. 55 detailed drawings carefully analyze outstanding pieces. "With its rich store of illustrations, this book emphasizes the individuality and varied design of early American pine furniture. It should be welcomed," ANTIQUES. 413 illustrations and 55 working drawings. 475. 8 x 10¾.　　　　　　　　　　T145 Clothbound **$10.00**

THE HUMAN FIGURE, J. H. Vanderpoel. Every important artistic element of the human figure is pointed out in minutely detailed word descriptions in this classic text and illustrated as well in 430 pencil and charcoal drawings. Thus the text of this book directs your attention to all the characteristic features and subtle differences of the male and female (adults, children, and aged persons), as though a master artist were telling you what to look for at each stage. 2nd edition, revised and enlarged by George Bridgman. Foreword. 430 illustrations. 143pp. 6⅛ x 9¼.　　　　　　　　　　T432 Paperbound **$1.50**

LETTERING AND ALPHABETS, J. A. Cavanagh. This unabridged reissue of LETTERING offers a full discussion, analysis, illustration of 89 basic hand lettering styles — styles derived from Caslons, Bodonis, Garamonds, Gothic, Black Letter, Oriental, and many others. Upper and lower cases, numerals and common signs pictured. Hundreds of technical hints on make-up, construction, artistic validity, strokes, pens, brushes, white areas, etc. May be reproduced without permission! 89 complete alphabets; 72 lettered specimens. 121pp. 9⅜ x 8.　　　　　　　　　　T53 Paperbound **$1.35**

STICKS AND STONES, Lewis Mumford. A survey of the forces that have conditioned American architecture and altered its forms. The author discusses the medieval tradition in early New England villages; the Renaissance influence which developed with the rise of the merchant class; the classical influence of Jefferson's time; the "Mechanicsvilles" of Poe's generation; the Brown Decades; the philosophy of the Imperial facade; and finally the modern machine age. "A truly remarkable book," SAT. REV. OF LITERATURE. 2nd revised edition. 21 illustrations. xvii + 228pp. 5⅜ x 8.　　　　　　　　　　T202 Paperbound **$2.00**

THE STANDARD BOOK OF QUILT MAKING AND COLLECTING, Marguerite Ickis. A complete easy-to-follow guide with all the information you need to make beautiful, useful quilts. How to plan, design, cut, sew, appliqué, avoid sewing problems, use rag bag, make borders, tuft, every other aspect. Over 100 traditional quilts shown, including over 40 full-size patterns. At-home hobby for fun, profit. Index. 483 illus. 1 color plate. 287pp. 6¾ x 9½.　　　　　　　　　　T582 Paperbound **$2.00**

THE BOOK OF SIGNS, Rudolf Koch. Formerly $20 to $25 on the out-of-print market, now only $1.00 in this unabridged new edition! 493 symbols from ancient manuscripts, medieval cathedrals, coins, catacombs, pottery, etc. Crosses, monograms of Roman emperors, astrological, chemical, botanical, runes, housemarks, and 7 other categories. Invaluable for handicraft workers, illustrators, scholars, etc., this material may be reproduced without permission. 493 illustrations by Fritz Kredel. 104pp. 6½ x 9¼.　　　　　　　　　　T162 Paperbound **$1.00**

PRIMITIVE ART, Franz Boas. This authoritative and exhaustive work by a great American anthropologist covers the entire gamut of primitive art. Pottery, leatherwork, metal work, stone work, wood, basketry, are treated in detail. Theories of primitive art, historical depth in art history, technical virtuosity, unconscious levels of patterning, symbolism, styles, literature, music, dance, etc. A must book for the interested layman, the anthropologist, artist, handicrafter (hundreds of unusual motifs), and the historian. Over 900 illustrations (50 ceramic vessels, 12 totem poles, etc.). 376pp. 5⅜ x 8.　　　　　　　　　　T25 Paperbound **$2.25**

Fiction

FLATLAND, E. A. Abbott. A science-fiction classic of life in a 2-dimensional world that is also a first-rate introduction to such aspects of modern science as relativity and hyperspace. Political, moral, satirical, and humorous overtones have made FLATLAND fascinating reading for thousands. 7th edition. New introduction by Banesh Hoffmann. 16 illustrations. 128pp. 5⅜ x 8.   T1 Paperbound **$1.00**

THE WONDERFUL WIZARD OF OZ, L. F. Baum. Only edition in print with all the original W. W. Denslow illustrations in full color—as much a part of "The Wizard" as Tenniel's drawings are of "Alice in Wonderland." "The Wizard" is still America's best-loved fairy tale, in which, as the author expresses it, "The wonderment and joy are retained and the heartaches and nightmares left out." Now today's young readers can enjoy every word and wonderful picture of the original book. New introduction by Martin Gardner. A Baum bibliography. 23 full-page color plates. viii + 268pp. 5⅜ x 8.   T691 Paperbound **$1.50**

THE MARVELOUS LAND OF OZ, L. F. Baum. This is the equally enchanting sequel to the "Wizard," continuing the adventures of the Scarecrow and the Tin Woodman. The hero this time is a little boy named Tip, and all the delightful Oz magic is still present. This is the Oz book with the Animated Saw-Horse, the Woggle-Bug, and Jack Pumpkinhead. All the original John R. Neill illustrations, 10 in full color. 287 pp. 5⅜ x 8.   T692 Paperbound **$1.50**

28 SCIENCE FICTION STORIES OF H. G. WELLS. Two full unabridged novels, MEN LIKE GODS and STAR BEGOTTEN, plus 26 short stories by the master science-fiction writer of all time! Stories of space, time, invention, exploration, future adventure—an indispensable part of the library of everyone interested in science and adventure. PARTIAL CONTENTS: Men Like Gods, The Country of the Blind, In the Abyss, The Crystal Egg, The Man Who Could Work Miracles, A Story of the Days to Come, The Valley of Spiders, and 21 more! 928pp. 5⅜ x 8.
T265 Clothbound **$4.50**

THREE MARTIAN NOVELS, Edgar Rice Burroughs. Contains: Thuvia, Maid of Mars; The Chessmen of Mars; and The Master Mind of Mars. High adventure set in an imaginative and intricate conception of the Red Planet. Mars is peopled with an intelligent, heroic human race which lives in densely populated cities and with fierce barbarians who inhabit dead sea bottoms. Other exciting creatures abound amidst an inventive framework of Martian history and geography. Complete unabridged reprintings of the first edition. 16 illustrations by J. Allen St. John. vi + 499pp. 5⅜ x 8½.   T39 Paperbound **$1.85**

SEVEN SCIENCE FICTION NOVELS, H. G. Wells. Full unabridged texts of 7 science-fiction novels of the master. Ranging from biology, physics, chemistry, astronomy to sociology and other studies, Mr. Wells extrapolates whole worlds of strange and intriguing character. "One will have to go far to match this for entertainment, excitement, and sheer pleasure . . . ," NEW YORK TIMES. Contents: The Time Machine, The Island of Dr. Moreau, First Men in the Moon, The Invisible Man, The War of the Worlds, The Food of the Gods, In the Days of the Comet. 1015pp. 5⅜ x 8.   T264 Clothbound **$5.00**

THE LAND THAT TIME FORGOT and THE MOON MAID, Edgar Rice Burroughs. In the opinion of many, Burroughs' best work. The first concerns a strange island where evolution is individual rather than phylogenetic. Speechless anthropoids develop into intelligent human beings within a single generation. The second projects the reader far into the future and describes the first voyage to the Moon (in the year 2025), the conquest of the Earth by the Moon, and years of violence and adventure as the enslaved Earthmen try to regain possession of their planet. "An imaginative tour de force that keeps the reader keyed up and expectant," NEW YORK TIMES. Complete, unabridged text of the original two novels (three parts in each). 5 illustrations by J. Allen St. John. vi + 552pp. 5⅜ x 8½.
T1020 Clothbound **$3.75**
T358 Paperbound **$2.00**

3 ADVENTURE NOVELS by H. Rider Haggard. Complete texts of "She," "King Solomon's Mines," "Allan Quatermain." Qualities of discovery; desire for immortality; search for primitive, for what is unadorned by civilization, have kept these novels of African adventure exciting, alive to readers from R. L. Stevenson to George Orwell. 636pp. 5⅜ x 8.
T584 Paperbound **$2.00**

A PRINCESS OF MARS and A FIGHTING MAN OF MARS: TWO MARTIAN NOVELS BY EDGAR RICE BURROUGHS. "Princess of Mars" is the very first of the great Martian novels written by Burroughs, and it is probably the best of them all; it set the pattern for all of his later fantasy novels and contains a thrilling cast of strange peoples and creatures and the formula of Olympian heroism amidst ever-fluctuating fortunes which Burroughs carries off so successfully. "Fighting Man" returns to the same scenes and cities—many years later. A mad scientist, a degenerate dictator, and an indomitable defender of the right clash—with the fate of the Red Planet at stake! Complete, unabridged reprinting of original editions. Illustrations by F. E. Schoonover and Hugh Hutton. v + 356pp. 5⅜ x 8½.
T1140 Paperbound **$1.75**

Music

A GENERAL HISTORY OF MUSIC, Charles Burney. A detailed coverage of music from the Greeks up to 1789, with full information on all types of music: sacred and secular, vocal and instrumental, operatic and symphonic. Theory, notation, forms, instruments, innovators, composers, performers, typical and important works, and much more in an easy, entertaining style. Burney covered much of Europe and spoke with hundreds of authorities and composers so that this work is more than a compilation of records . . . it is a living work of careful and first-hand scholarship. Its account of thoroughbass (18th century) Italian music is probably still the best introduction on the subject. A recent NEW YORK TIMES review said, "Surprisingly few of Burney's statements have been invalidated by modern research . . . still of great value." Edited and corrected by Frank Mercer. 35 figures. Indices. 1915pp. 5⅜ x 8. 2 volumes. T36 The Set, Clothbound **$15.00**

A DICTIONARY OF HYMNOLOGY, John Julian. This exhaustive and scholarly work has become known as an invaluable source of hundreds of thousands of important and often difficult to obtain facts on the history and use of hymns in the western world. Everyone interested in hymns will be fascinated by the accounts of famous hymns and hymn writers and amazed by the amount of practical information he will find. More than 30,000 entries on individual hymns, giving authorship, date and circumstances of composition, publication, textual variations, translations, denominational and ritual usage, etc. Biographies of more than 9,000 hymn writers, and essays on important topics such as Christmas carols and children's hymns, and much other unusual and valuable information. A 200 page double-columned index of first lines — the largest in print. Total of 1786 pages in two reinforced clothbound volumes. 6¼ x 9¼.
The set, T333 Clothbound **$17.50**

MUSIC IN MEDIEVAL BRITAIN, F. Ll. Harrison. The most thorough, up-to-date, and accurate treatment of the subject ever published, beautifully illustrated. Complete account of institutions and choirs; carols, masses, and motets; liturgy and plainsong; and polyphonic music from the Norman Conquest to the Reformation. Discusses the various schools of music and their reciprocal influences; the origin and development of new ritual forms; development and use of instruments; and new evidence on many problems of the period. Reproductions of scores, over 200 excerpts from medieval melodies. Rules of harmony and dissonance; influence of Continental styles; great composers (Dunstable, Cornysh, Fairfax, etc.); and much more. Register and index of more than 400 musicians. Index of titles. General Index. 225-item bibliography. 6 Appendices. xix + 491pp. 5⅝ x 8¾. T705 Clothbound **$10.00**

THE MUSIC OF SPAIN, Gilbert Chase. Only book in English to give concise, comprehensive account of Iberian music; new Chapter covers music since 1941. Victoria, Albéniz, Cabezón, Pedrell, Turina, hundreds of other composers; popular and folk music; the Gypsies; the guitar; dance, theatre, opera, with only extensive discussion in English of the Zarzuela; virtuosi such as Casals; much more. "Distinguished . . . readable," Saturday Review. 400-item bibliography. Index. 27 photos. 383pp. 5⅜ x 8. T549 Paperbound **$2.25**

ON STUDYING SINGING, Sergius Kagen. An intelligent method of voice-training, which leads you around pitfalls that waste your time, money, and effort. Exposes rigid, mechanical systems, baseless theories, deleterious exercises. "Logical, clear, convincing . . . dead right," Virgil Thomson, N.Y. Herald Tribune. "I recommend this volume highly," Maggie Teyte, Saturday Review. 119pp. 5⅜ x 8. T622 Paperbound **$1.35**

Prices subject to change without notice.

Dover publishes books on art, music, philosophy, literature, languages, history, social sciences, psychology, handcrafts, orientalia, puzzles and entertainments, chess, pets and gardens, books explaining science, intermediate and higher mathematics, mathematical physics, engineering, biological sciences, earth sciences, classics of science, etc. Write to:

Dept. catrr.
Dover Publications, Inc.
180 Varick Street, N.Y. 14, N.Y.